All Colour World of FARM ANIMALS

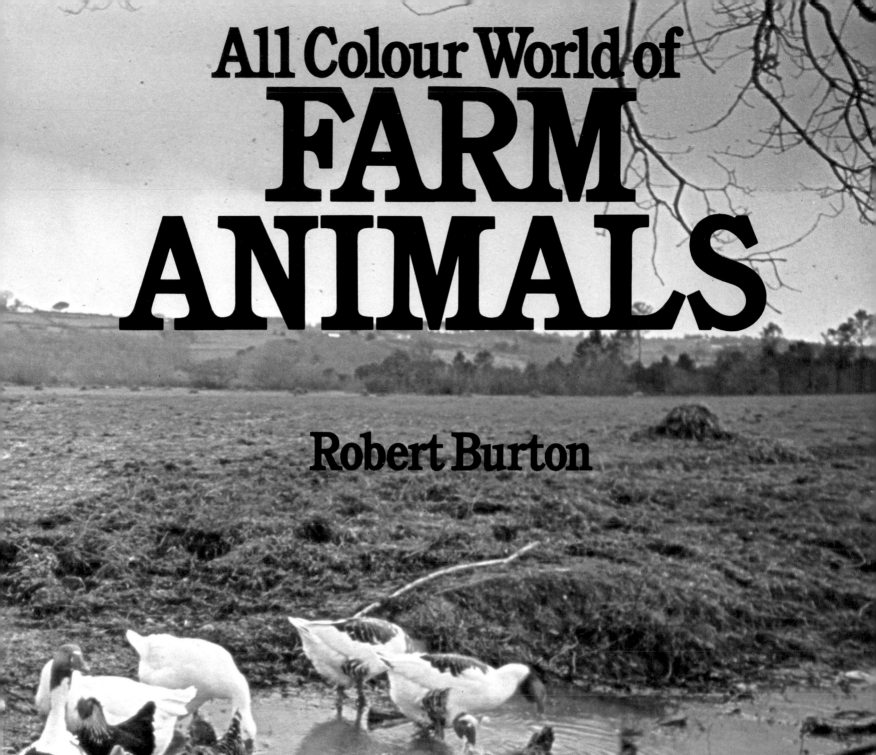

All Colour World of
FARM ANIMALS

Robert Burton

octopus

Contents

First published 1979 by Octopus Books Limited
59 Grosvenor Street, London W1

© 1979 Octopus Books Limited

ISBN 0 7064 1008 4

Produced by Mandarin Publishers Limited
22a Westlands Road
Quarry Bay, Hong Kong

Printed in Hong Kong

The History of Farm Animals

Long ago, our ancestors roamed the forests and grassy plains living a simple existence that differed little from the animals around them. Gradually, as the centuries passed, successive generations forced a gap between human beings and animals. Using three unique characters – a large brain, a spoken language and a dextrous hand – primitive men set about establishing their supremacy over animals. They invented tools which acted as extensions of the body, and made the wielding arm more powerful. Also they discovered the value of fire. At this stage of evolution, Man was a hunter and gatherer. Language had made possible co-operative hunting and gathering of food.

There are still people living a simple life of hunting and gathering. They include the Arctic Eskimos, the Aborigines of Australia, the African Bushmen and the Yaghan of Tierra del Fuego. To describe them as primitive does not mean that they are uncultured, but they have clearly failed to exploit the environment at the same pace as the rest of us. Hunters and collectors are at one with nature; the rest of mankind exploits it. The hunters were left behind from the broad flow of human advance because they never took up farming. Farming, or agriculture, is the deliberate manipulation of animals and plants for food. Certain plants and herds of livestock are favoured at the expense of 'weeds' and 'pests' which are vigorously attacked.

The rise in living standards caused by the introduction of farming animals and plants has been well described as the most important 'revolution' in human history. More food enabled the population to grow. Settled communities were formed and urban life started. Some people were freed from the drudgery of food production to become specialists in arts and crafts. Nevertheless, the majority of the population was tied to the land until two centuries ago.

Left: The Indian buffalo, or water buffalo, is a form of domestic cattle native to India and South-east Asia. Descended from the fierce wild buffalo, they are reared for meat and milk.

Right: There are very few wild asses alive in the wild today. The race of African wild ass which gave rise to the domestic donkey is now extinct. The first domestic asses were used as beasts of burden and for milk.

Then, a dramatic change in the pattern of life which has become known as the Industrial Revolution started in western Europe and spread around the world. The invention of new machines and processes increased the production of goods and led to the formation of a new urban class of artisans. Yet the Industrial Revolution could not have taken place without the Agricultural Revolution which preceded it. This had a two-fold effect. First, new agricultural practices increased productivity on the farms which enabled the countryside to support the mushrooming urban populations. Second, the new practices required a smaller work force, so men were freed from the land (in some cases driven from it by their landlords) and they migrated to the towns to provide labour in the new factories.

The agricultural revolution is still continuing as the increased mechanization of farms reduces the work-force still further and we have entered the era of factory-farming, where the Industrial and Agricultural Revolutions have linked up. The modern mechanized farm is now a far cry from the traditional view of a farm and its animals. The 'farmyard' of our schoolbooks, with its assortment of cows, pigs, horses and chickens is a scene that has almost disappeared. It belonged to the two centuries following the Agricultural Revolution, when the small-holdings of the peasants were replaced by large, centralized farms and it was ousted by the specializations that have developed in the last 30 years.

All over the country there are abandoned farm-yards, useful only for storing farm machinery and bags of fertilizer. The trend in farming, as in other industries, has been strongly directed to uniformity, which makes for ease of management and simpler marketing. But in recent years there have been signs of a reversal of this trend.

A growing band of people who have become dissatisfied with urban life buy small farms and smallholdings which they run with the intention of being as 'self-sufficient' as possible. To achieve this, they have to keep a variety of farm animals to meet the owner's own needs or to sell so they can buy necessities not provided by the farm. This is a policy as old as farming itself.

Another reason for diversifying is to deliberately offset the trend in modern farming of concentrating on very few breeds of farm animals. At one time there was a wide range of breeds, each one developed for a particular purpose and often bred in one region to fit that area's particular set of farming conditions. Many of these old breeds are dying out. Their characters are no longer valued on modern farms but there is good reason to conserve these stocks. Apart from the aesthetic appeal of maintaining a breed, it could happen that changing circumstances in the farming world could bring its peculiar characteristics back to favour. Without a 'bank' of these old breeds to call upon, these characters will be lost for ever.

Before investigating in detail the histories, habits and uses of the many farm animals, it is interesting to

look into the origins of farming and the domestication of animals. What prompted our forebears to keep and control animals and what influenced their choice of animals to be domesticated?

The origins of domestication are lost in the dawn of civilization. Animal husbandry started before written records were kept. The story can be pieced together only from archaeological finds and from the farming methods used by primitive peoples which have yet to be changed by the spread of modern farming. For close on two million years the entire, but very scant, population of the world were hunters and gatherers. Then there was a revolution. During the period known as the New Stone Age, the population increased and farming started. The two are inseparable; it is impossible to say whether rising populations made a more efficient exploitation of the land necessary or whether the inventions of agriculture resulted in more food and a longer life for farmers. The latter explanation seems to be most likely. Be that as it may, the key to this huge change in the human condition lay in the improvement of climate as the glaciers of the last Ice Age retreated northwards. But human society also had to have reached a level of

organization for farming to become practicable.

There have been several suggestions as to how man first entered into his intimate relationship with animals. Up to this time, he had been a hunter. His aim had been to get close to animals so that he could kill them. Domestication consists of getting close to animals and letting them live. One suggestion has been that animals were kept for religious purposes, for later sacrifice or as 'mascots' to help in hunting. Little support can be found for this notion and the two most likely theories are that captive animals were either used as decoys to lure their wild relatives within range of the hunters or that they were kept as walking food stores to be slaughtered and eaten when needed.

Support for these ideas comes from the practices of contemporary primitive peoples. Both Australian aborigines and the Red Indians of North America have been accustomed to keeping animals as living larders. The animals need not be kept permanently in captivity. There is a long tradition for leaving herds of animals to roam freely and to round them up at intervals. In Britain, the ponies of the New Forest and the sheep of Highland Scotland are still managed in this way.

The use of captive animals as decoys when hunting has been used by the Samoyeds and Tungus of northern USSR. Both tribes are reindeer hunters and they employed a number of stratagems based on the natural behaviour of the deer. Samoyed hunters used their tame reindeer as camouflage, holding them on short ropes so that they could approach a wild herd and get within range of bow and arrow without arousing suspicion. Sometimes the hinds were left to roam free in the rutting season. They were joined by wild stags which could then be stalked with comparative ease. Another ploy in the rutting season was to liberate a stag with ropes attached to its antlers. It would engage in a fight with a wild stag, and their antlers got knotted together. Red deer were caught by similar means in mediaeval Germany, and European bison and the aurochs, the extinct ancestor of domestic cattle, were hunted in this fashion.

We can think of the first steps in domestication being rather haphazard and irregular. Compassionate hunters brought in orphans of the animals which they had killed, but they must have hard-headedly realized the value of taming a young animal and feeding it up, perhaps on scraps, to provide an easy source of high grade food. The use of these animals as decoys could well have followed as the animals gradually became tame. However, casual animal keeping is not farming.

Far left: According to some, the mouflon is the wild sheep most closely related to domestic sheep. It lives in Corsica and Sardinia and is the smallest and most colourful of all sheep.

Left: Goats are the oldest farm animals. Present-day farm goats are descended from the bezoar goat or pasang goat which now survives only as the Cretan wild goat.

9

Farming involves the systematic taming and keeping of animals for the practical purposes of providing food, locomotive power and raw materials. Domestication also involves, by definition, the breeding of animals in captivity so that the captive stock becomes completely isolated from their wild forbears. Once this independence is achieved, selective breeding can take place and the stock is 'improved'. This makes the animals better suited for farm use by improving their breeding rate, growth rate and the production of meat, milk and so on.

In the search for the origins of systematic animal keeping, attention has been focused on the Near East, particularly the region between Turkey, Palestine, Afghanistan and Iran. This includes Mesopotamia, the once fertile region of the Euphrates and Tigris rivers known as the Fertile Crescent, where the ancient civilizations of Ur, Assyria and Babylon flourished. The Nile Valley, parts of China and, in the New World, Middle America are also early centres of farming. The pattern for the evolution of farming seems to have been for arable or crop farming to precede stock or animal farming and that arable farming started in mountainous districts and was later taken to the low-lying, fertile plains. Wild wheat and barley grew naturally in broad swathes in the mountain, where the hunting, gathering tribes would have learned to harvest the ripe grains. The next step was to plant seeds in prepared ground where weeds and animal pests could be kept out.

Not surprisingly, plots of crops attracted the attentions of large plant-eating animals. One such was the wild goat. The mountains of eastern Europe and the Near East were the home of the bezoar goat, which still survives on the island of Crete. The early agriculturists would probably have hunted wild goats to supplement their crops and they would certainly have hunted any goats poaching these crops. This sets the scene for the keeping of orphans and the discovery of how easy it is to tame young animals. Then, they found that it is so much easier to keep tame herds than to go out hunting. As for keeping animals as living food-stores, it is interesting that some mountain people still feed their surplus grain to their goats.

Putting a date to the origin of animal farming has proved difficult because there is no difference between the bones of wild animals and those that had recently been domesticated. Only when bodily proportions have been altered by selective breeding is it possible to label a collection of bones from an archaeological site as being from domesticated animals. There are other clues, however. Bones of the bezoar goat have been found in 9,000-year-old settlements in Mesopotamia and neighbouring Palestine. These settlements are in flat country far removed from the mountain home of the bezoar goat. Therefore, the remains must be those of domesticated animals. In comparison agricultural implements from Mesopotamia show that the harvesting of crops took place 2,000 years earlier, if not more.

The difficulty with identifying bones dug from prehistoric man's middens raises a second problem in the history of domestication: literally that of sorting sheep from goats. It is not easy to distinguish between these two animals. The main difference is in the shape of the horns and in the tail. In goats, the horns are the same in males and females, whereas male sheep have larger horns than do females, and the horns of the goat do not spread out as they do in sheep. The tail sweeps upward in goats, downward in sheep. Other differences include the billy goats beard and the gland under the tail which gives the billy its characteristic pungent smell. These latter characteristics are, of course, no use in identifying remains thousands of years old. The main difference in the skeleton are the stouter, shorter bones in the goat's legs. This is a reflection of the difference in their ways of life. Goats live in rocky places and need strong legs to stand up to the constant jarring of jumping whereas sheep live in flatter country and have longer, more slender legs for speedy, sustained running.

A study of bone remains, and of cave paintings, shows that, before 10,000 BC, sheep are mysteriously absent. One explanation is that there was no such animal in existence and that sheep only evolved from goats during the era of these Near East settlements. Investigations into the genetics of the two animals suggest that sheep could have arisen from a sudden mutation, or genetic change, in goats.

If this theory is correct, sheep could either have arisen from wild goats and have been domesticated almost immediately or they could have developed from domestic goats. The several types of wild sheep, such as the Barbary sheep of North Africa and the bighorn sheep of America are no more than descendents of domestic sheep which went wild. The existence of bighorn sheep is evidence of the fast spread of sheep domestication. Sheep must have travelled from the Near East to North America before 7,000 BC, when the Bering Strait (which separates the land mass of Asia and the North American continent) opened up. After this it would have been impossible for the animals to cross from continent to continent.

Rapid domestication and spread of sheep is quite possible because they have several characteristics which make them better domestic animals than goats. They prefer flat grasslands to rocky slopes; they eat grass and shun the leaves of bushes; and, in particular, they readily form large herds. It is not surprising that sheep have far outstripped goats in importance as farm animals, except in barren and rocky regions.

The theory that goats, and perhaps sheep, became domesticated after they had taken to raiding crops is not held by all authorities. An alternative is that their association with man started when he was a nomadic hunter. The herds of animals were also nomadic and man learned to follow the herds. He killed sufficient animals to satisfy his needs and in return protected the herd from wolves and other carnivores. Gradually the two species were drawn together as man took control and subjugated the animal. It is possible that the horse was domesticated in this manner by nomads on the grassy steppes, and the reindeer of the tundra developed an association with Arctic tribes. Reindeer herds continue their wanderings to this day and the Lapps continue a nomadic life. They follow the free-ranging deer and round them up once a year.

While there is difference of opinion over the method of domesticating sheep and goats, the domestication of cattle appears to have been more straightforward. The wild ancestor of domestic cattle, the aurochs, was domesticated after it had become a crop robber. The earliest known domestic cattle come from remains in Greece and Turkey dated to 6,000 BC. They proved to be productive and easily kept, so that cattle soon became the most important of all farm animals.

The pig may also have been a crop robber, but it was also drawn to human settlements to root through refuse for scraps. In this respect it followed the pattern of such different animals as dogs and ducks. All three species are natural scavengers which would have been attracted to refuse heaps and odd scraps. Once they have taken to entering settlements, it is only

a short step to encouraging them by putting out food and exploiting them by systematic cropping. The dog is an exception to other domestic animals mentioned so far. Although undoubtedly killed for food at times, early man recognized the value of the dog's natural behaviour of rounding up herds of animals and selecting one beast from the crowd. So man used dogs first to help in his hunts and then to help control domestic herds and flocks.

So far we have seen two stages of domestication. First there was a loose association of Man and animal, with the former exploiting the latter. Then the animals were confined and bred in captivity. Frederick Zeuner, the authority on the history of domestication, sees a further three stages in domestication. Once breeding takes place in captivity, the early farmers could start to select particular traits in their animals and farm animals began to appear which differed physically from the wild types. Domestic animals acquired bold patchwork colour schemes quite unlike the drab patterns suitable for camouflage found in wild animals. Their dangerous horns were usually reduced, as was the overall body size. By 3,000 BC, the Near-eastern civilizations had advanced to the fourth stage of domestication and were deliberately creating 'breeds' of farm animals for particular purposes.

Farms now flourished at a greater rate. Herds and flocks needed more space to graze and browse as the human population expanded. With this increased food supply, farmers found that their stock were competing with the wild progenitors. The final stage of domestication saw the extermination of the animals which had helped Man through the great revolution from a hand-to-mouth existence into organized civilization. Some of the original stocks have gone. The aurochs is extinct; the tarpan – the wild horse of Europe – was killed off because tame mares were being seduced away by wild stallions; and wild pigs, asses, goats and sheep have become increasingly rare. If they are not killed off, they are captured and brought into the fold.

Given hundreds of wild animals to choose from, only a handful of species are domesticated. The common farm animals are cattle, horses and donkeys,

sheep, goats and pigs, chickens, turkeys, geese and ducks. If we think about it, others spring to mind. Bees and silkmoths are domesticated insects. Fish are farmed in colossal numbers particularly in warm parts of the world. Pigeons and rabbits were an important source of meat in winter before the invention of refrigeration. Guineafowl are farmed for special occasions or specialized palates. In different parts of the world, camels, elephants, yaks and llamas suit local conditions.

In past times, a variety of strange animals were brought into domestication. The Ancient Egyptians fattened hyaenas for the table, as did the Romans with dormice; mongooses joined cats in the war against rodents. South Africans farmed ostriches for their plumes and prehistoric lake-dwellers of Switzerland even domesticated foxes. None of these animals were a great success as farm animals but the search for new farm animals continues. Red deer are herded in the Scottish Highlands and English parks and eland, a large antelope, are farmed on African savannahs.

What is the key to successful domestication? Apart from their ability to provide us with useful commodities, farm animals behave in a way that makes them easy to manage. There are certain aspects of the behaviour of the wild animal which lend themselves to domestication. These are considered in some detail in the next chapter.

Follow the Leader

On a modern, intensive 'factory' farm, it would seem that an animal has little chance of expressing its personality. Its life is ordered from birth to death within the confines of a very unnatural existence. Clearly a battery chicken, or a calf that never enjoys a run in a pasture, are not leading the lives of their wild ancestors but it is wrong to think that they are mere robots. If anything, it has become more necessary to understand the behaviour of farm animals if they are to flourish on a crowded modern farm.

There is one habit shared by all farm animals which is obvious with a moment's thought. Farm animals are social animals. We speak of herds of cattle and horses, flocks of sheep and poultry. They live harmoniously together in close knit groups. If it were not for this fact, farming would be virtually impossible. Animals could not be easily driven from place to place and they could not be penned together. As Charles Darwin wrote: 'complete subjugation generally depends on an animal being social in its habits, and on receiving man as the chief of the herd or family'. Most farm animals belong to three groups: the hoofed mammals, the chickens and their relatives in the game-bird group, and the waterfowl. It is no coincidence that all three usually live in herds or flocks.

At first sight a herd of cows lying in the corner of a field, chewing the cud, a dense flock of sheep pouring over the brow of a hill or chickens roosting snugly on a perch appears to be a classless, wholly egalitarian society. Nothing could be further from the truth.

Left: Farm animals live in flocks and herds. Their natural instinct is to keep together, which makes it easy for them to be controlled. It is only necessary to guide the leading animal in the right direction for the others to follow in an orderly fashion. Farm animals are also creatures of habit and lead lives of regular routine. These Jersey cows are making their way to the milking parlour. They will have been waiting for the gate of their field to be opened and, without further guidance, they walk to their stalls.

Right: Farm animals like to be comfortable and will try to keep from getting too hot or cold. These pigs are wallowing in a muddy puddle not because they like filth but to keep cool on a hot day.

Animal societies are as ordered as any devised by a dictator. There is a leader who has undisputed authority over inferiors whose ranking is military in its organization. The impression of a formless society is dispelled by occasional bickering between the animals. There is rarely any serious fighting. Often one animal does no more than walk up to another, who gets up and moves away. At other times there is a greater show of aggression: horses bare their teeth, cattle butt head to head and chickens peck but no harm is done. The rigid social status of the animals actually prevents fighting because each animal knows its place in society and defers to its seniors. Without this discipline, life in the flock or herd would become impossible. At every occasion, at feeding troughs or when passing through gates, there would be arguments about which animal should take precedence.

The social system in a group of animals is often called a 'peck order' because it was first studied among poultry where a chicken disciplines its inferiors with a peck. In the peck order of a flock of barnyard fowls, hen A pecks B, but, on no account, will B peck A. However B can peck C and C pecks D. D can peck E, F, G and so on through the flock, but D cannot peck A, B and C. The peck order is not obvious for most of the time. Once in a while, a hen pecks irritably at

Above: The pitiful bleat of a lamb shows that it is lost, scared and hungry. The call alerts its mother who may be out of sight and it helps her to find her lamb among the mass of sheep. Once reunited, the bleats cease because the lamb gets security from the nearness of its mother. Adult sheep bleat when they are separated from their close companions.

Left: These Romney Marsh sheep are sheltering in the shade of a tree, while they rest and chew the cud. Trees help the sheep to keep cool in summer and act as a windbreak where the sheep can huddle to keep warm in winter.

another that comes too close. Overall, life in the hen run is peaceful. But throw in a handful of grain, and the peck order is quickly revealed. The hens rush over and start to snap up grains furiously. They jostle together but one bird always gets the best feeding position. The others take care not to impose upon her. This is hen A, the flock leader. Around the edge of the cluster of hens, there will be a few who look rather shy and uncomfortable. They are at the bottom of the peck order and they crane forward gingerly to peck at grains, ready to retreat or crouch submissively the moment one of their betters turns on them. These chickens at the bottom of the peck order are almost

social outcasts, pecked by everyone and unable to peck back, and their lowly status is reflected by the poor condition of their plumage.

When a new flock of chickens is started, there is considerable fighting. The birds are strangers and each seeks to assert itself. Over a period of several days, the strife dies down. Each chicken has learned its place. As with people, chickens recognize each other by the appearance of the head. A hen sometimes mistakenly pecks a superior if the latter has her head hidden.

The peck order rarely changes once it has been established and the flock settles to an orderly existence and every bird learns to accept its position. How the birds decide who is dominant over whom is not easy to see. Some are naturally more aggressive and older birds tend to be the more senior, but the peck order can be shuffled artificially. If hen A is removed from the flock, B takes over as leader. After two weeks the rest of the hens will have forgotten A and when replaced she has to accept a lower rank. The peck order can even be reversed. If the lowest hen is isolated in a new run for one week and the others added one at a time in reverse order of rank, the former lowest ranker emerges as leader.

Peck orders are found in groups of cattle, horses, sheep and goats and pigs. When strange cattle are pastured together ranks are worked out on a basis of age and physical strength but the ranking is often more complicated than the simple A butts B butts C system. It can be quite complicated, particularly among the inferior animals. F may be superior to G, and G to H but a triangle is then formed by H being superior to F. Society is also complicated when both sexes live together. In mixed herds it is usual for males and females to form separate peck orders, but females usually defer to males. In large herds the social structure either becomes increasingly complex or breaks down into small 'sub-herds'. A large flock of sheep is an unnatural gathering but, if left alone, the sheep try to stay near their relatives or other familiar animals. The continual 'baa-ing' coming from a large flock is caused by sheep being separated from their companions.

The member of a society of farm animals is continually keeping watch on its fellows. Apart from making sure that it does not incur the displeasure of its superiors or suffer the intrusion of its inferiors, it keeps watch on the activities of its fellows and, despite

the security of the farm, it watches out for enemies. The behaviour of a flock of sheep is well coordinated. They graze at the same time, they rest together and the flock travels as a unit.

'Behaving like sheep' is the expression used to describe human beings who blindly follow a leader. It has a sound basis. If one sheep starts to walk, its neighbours start to follow and the rest join in. There is no true leader but, in a flock of sheep for instance, the older ewes usually take the lead with their lambs and older offspring, and their lambs, following. When one of these extended families starts to move, it draws the rest of the flock with it.

Left: Two rams butting is a means of deciding social standing and most likely to take place between two rams of almost equal status. If one ram is very much superior it does not have to resort to a fight to show its position.

Below: A Wheaten Old English Game bantam sunbathes with her chicks. This performs a useful function. When a bird preens, it spreads oil from the preen gland over the feathers. Sunlight converts constituents of the oil into vitamin D which is swallowed by the bird when next it preens.

Relations between the members of a flock or herd are ordered by exchanging signals. They are talking, if you like, but the conversation is either bickering or small gestures of reassurance. The animals show their feelings by grimaces and body movements, expressions which tell a simple message. Understanding an animal's mood by watching its face is of practical importance to anyone who handles horses, when it is vital to know whether they are likely to kick or bite. The ears turned back is a sign of aggression; turned forward shows friendly intentions. Bared teeth shows hostility, and if the tail is flicked – watch out for a kick.

Facial expressions and body postures are joined by various calls which are most used for long distance communication. We have seen how sheep *baa* when they are separated from their close companions. They are trying to make contact and they are afraid. The horse's *neigh* is similarly a distress signal heard when companions are separated. When reunited they *nicker* in relief. A *snort* is a far-carrying danger signal and a *whinny* is for greeting: 'Hello! It's you'.

Friendly relations between farm animals are often cemented by the animals grooming one another.

Cattle lick each other and horses nibble one another's withers. Cattle usually lick socially superior companions and being licked must be pleasurable because cows will solicit patting and scratching around head and neck from humans. Horses, on the other hand, are often loath to be petted. Sensitive horses, that are unaccustomed to handling, particularly resent being touched on the head, belly and legs.

Life on the farm is routine. Food – hay, swill, or whatever – is put out at regular times, milking has its set times and the farm animals get used to a timetable. They can anticipate the arrival of the farmer and line up ready for feeding or milking. In countries where the clocks are changed at the beginning and ending of summer, farm animals are thrown out by the change in routine.

But even without these man-imposed constraints, farm animals lead regular lives. Cattle and sheep spend about six hours a day grazing, mostly during the day but also at night during warm weather. Feeding time is divided into a number of 'bouts'. The herd acts together, moving slowly across the pasture, cropping the grass as they go. All stop grazing at the same time, they go to drink together (especially after milking) and they chew the cud together. The rest of the day is spent in idleness.

Cattle spend as much as 12 out of 24 hours lying down, particularly if they can find shade from hot sun.

Above: The companionable nature of farm animals is shown by this donkey and a Heidschnucke sheep. Even in a flock, an animal will tend to spend its time with a few particular friends and, if kept apart from a herd, it will strike up a relationship with another kind of animal.

Right: Apart from reaching the parts an animal cannot lick itself, grooming fulfils a social function. Cattle usually groom their social superiors who appear to enjoy the operation.

Yet, strange as it may seem, they rarely, if ever, sleep. Their eyelids may drop and close for a while, the head drops and the ears flop but experimenters have found that there is no true sleep, as we understand the term. The same is true of sheep and goats but horses sleep soundly for several hours a day. They usually sleep standing up and each 'nap' is very short.

Bad weather drives farm animals to seek the shelter of wind breaks where they huddle morosely together. Moorland sheep find shelter under peathags but in a field the best shelter is obtained from other members of the herd. Horses get extra protection in winter by rolling so that a weatherproof layer of dirt accumulates in their winter coats. In summer wallowing helps keep the body cool. This is most noticeable in pigs and when they are confined to the sty this habit earns them their reputation for dirty habits. They root up the ground so that they can lie against the cooler subsoil but they much prefer to wallow in puddles. In cold weather pigs huddle together to preserve heat.

Animals at Work

Although it is not certain whether the first domestic animals were kept as decoys or for food, it is reasonably certain that using the strength of animals to relieve man of his burdens was introduced at a later stage. At some time it must have occurred to nomads that they could load their household goods onto the backs of their animals and so save themselves a great deal of effort. This is one of the uses to which the Lapps put their reindeer.

Turning an animal from a walking larder into a living wheelbarrow was made possible through a great step forward in the relationship between man and the animal. In the former case, the herdsman relies on his animals' natural herd instincts to keep together and he merely has to guide them. The animals need to be only sufficiently tame for the herdsman to approach closely and perhaps handle them. To become a carrier, the animal must be extremely docile. It must learn to obey a few simple orders and it has to learn to accept the load and the securing harness. Only when training had become sufficiently sophisticated were animals able to accept another animal – Man – upon their backs or to be harnessed to sledges and carts.

The use of animals as carriers started well before the invention of the wheel. The first carriers were pack animals in which the load was secured to the animals' backs, with some form of padding as a saddle. That this is the simplest way in which animals have been made to work is seen from the many kinds which are used for this purpose. Apart from cattle, and horses and donkeys, there are in use around the world as pack animals: reindeer, yaks, elephants, camels, llamas, dogs, even, in the Himalayan region, sheep and goats.

Left: Two pairs of strong and reliable Shire horses draw a mechanical reaper – a scene which has now almost vanished. The reaper has been replaced by the combine harvester, but the first combines were pulled by teams of mules. The Shire is the largest breed of heavy horse and can be recognized by the amount of 'feathering', the hairy 'leggings' on the lower part of the limbs.

Right: Most cats lead a pampered, idle existence but this farm cat enjoying a scratch in the sun earns its living by catching rats and mice.

Cattle were the first animals to be used for regular work by farmers, rather than as carriers, although they were domesticated for food after sheep, goats and pigs. Cows and bulls are sometimes used but the usual beast of burden is the ox, a bull which has been castrated to render it docile. Cattle came into use as working farm animals in prehistoric times, and the earliest records show them performing useful tasks. Seals found in the temples of Mesopotamia show that cattle carried loads on their backs and dragged sledges about 5,000 years ago. They were also used for thrashing corn: the sheaves were laid on a solid floor and a cow was forced to walk around until its cloven hoofs had stamped out the grains. Ox-drawn ploughs and, with the invention of the wheel, carts followed not long afterwards. Not for another two millenia were oxen challenged as heavy draught animals and only within the last thousand years have horses increasingly replaced oxen as the draught animals of the western world. Even now oxen are still important in many places.

The harness used throughout history to secure oxen to a plough or cart is the yoke. Oxen nearly always worked in pairs and the word yoke means, in fact, 'to join'. Because of its connotations with a life of drudgery 'yoke' has come to mean servitude, subjugation, even marriage!

A yoke is a solid beam of wood, carved to fit over the shoulders of the oxen, the weight of the load is taken on the withers, the 'hump' between the shoulders. A vertical bar of wood on each side of the neck prevents the yoke from slipping off and a rope or bar under the neck prevents the cart from tipping and lifting the yoke off. The yoke is fixed to a pole leading from the plough or cart. In a few places the shoulder yoke is not used and the harness consists of a breastband or of a small yoke, padded with skins, placed around the horns or neck. Elsewhere, a collar rather like a horse

Right: Working horses have been almost completely ousted by motor transport, but even in towns horses, particularly brewers' horses, can still be seen doing a useful job.

Below: Product of a female horse and a male donkey, a mule is a very sturdy, intelligent beast of burden. A hinny is the less familiar offspring of a male horse and a female ass. Mules have been used for centuries to carry packs or draw vehicles.

collar is used. Like horses, oxen need protection for their hoofs when working on built-up roads. The cloven hoofs of oxen are more difficult to shoe than the horse's single hoof but oxen are fitted with double or single shoes where the going is hard.

In mediaeval times oxen were used for ploughing and drawing carts, and breeds were developed to suit local conditions. Long-legged, slender oxen worked on light soils and pulled lighter loads but solid, thickset creatures were needed for ploughing clay. As essential sidelines, these draught animals were valued for their hides and meat when they got too old to work and the use of cows for heavy work did not release them from calf bearing and milk production.

The use of oxen as plough animals has left a mark on the countryside – which can still be seen in parts of rural Britain. Traces of mediaeval or earlier open-field systems have survived the patterns of modern farming imposed upon them. They are easily recognised from the air and can be discerned from the ground during spells of very dry weather. As the soil dries out the plant cover withers unevenly and the ridges and furrows begin to stand out.

The characteristic feature of these ancient ox-ploughed fields is that they curve in a gentle reverse S. The plough was drawn by pairs of oxen, with up to four pairs linked together, depending on the heaviness of the soil. The ox-team was an unwieldy unit and turning the plough at the end of the field (the headland) was tedious. To make things easier, the team was guided in a gentle curve so that it was already partly turned when it reached the headland and it would set off again before the circle had been completed. The furrows were always turned in the same direction so the traces of ancient fields always show the same orientation.

The unwieldiness of the ox-team was also responsible for the long, narrow shape of old fields. Because turning was laborious the field was ploughed in strips, which represented a day's work. The area was called an acre, which in those days varied from place to place depending, again, on how easily the soil could be worked. The length of the strip was one furrow-long or furlong and the breadth was one tenth of this. Eventually these measurements became standardized with a furlong of 220 yards. The breadth of the strip became a chain of 22 yards, so the acre is 4,840 square yards. These units still exist in the measurements of racecourses, and in the 22 yard cricket pitch, and they demonstrate that the old British system of measurement was not haphazard but deeply rooted in everyday and vital aspects of people's lives.

Right: Even when resting, this collie is alert for the moment when her services will be needed. Sheepdogs are the one working animal which will never be replaced by a machine. No other animal has reached such a high standard of skill and obedience. Bred purely as a working dog and not for their appearance, collies are never seen as show animals and their temperament does not make them the best of pets.

Far right: At a sheepdog trials, a shepherd and his collie show their skills. The aim of the exercise is for the dog to guide the sheep around a course of obstacles, including going between the gates in the background. Finally, the sheep are coaxed into the pen and the gate is shut. The shepherd is not allowed to move and orders the dog with whistles.

Ploughmen called the day's work a journey, an apparently odd name but it comes from the mediaeval *jurnalis*, itself a corruption of the Latin *diurnalis*.

The ox-team was worked by two men. The ploughman was concerned with guiding his implement while the animals were tended by the driver who was armed with a long goad. He walked either alongside the team or ahead of them, going backwards so as to face them, and kept up a constant stream of exhortation. There were even special songs for the purpose. Pulling a plough through heavy soil is a strenuous activity even for such powerful animals as oxen so their working hours were limited. As they suffered under a hot sun the policy was to make an early start, before dawn for much of the year. Ploughing continued until midday and the oxen were then unyoked and returned to the stable. The old German term for the area ploughed in one day was *morgen* (morning). This procedure was clearly more efficient than having to unyoke the oxen, a long business with a team of eight, rest them and reharness them for a second stint in the afternoon.

Ploughing with oxen survived in Britain well into the 20th century. The last oxen were taken out of service and replaced by tractors in 1951 on Fair Isle which lies between Orkney and Shetland, off the north coast of Scotland. Elsewhere in Europe, particularly in the south and east, oxen are still widely used. The horse was not the obvious substitute draught animal that it might seem at first sight and 'horse versus ox' was an argument that continued among farmers during the 18th and 19th centuries. Horses were faster than oxen but needed more care and attention. Oxen survived on poorer food, could start work at a younger age and then be sold profitably for meat when past their prime. At the end of the 18th century some English farmers replaced their Shire horses with oxen.

Perhaps the main reason for using oxen as draught animals in age or place is that they are cheaper. In Saxon times an ox was worth 30 silver pence and a horse half a pound of silver. Horses were used exclusively for riding. In these times they would probably have been too small and weak for heavy farm labour. Only when fighting men became heavily armoured was the strong 'heavy' horse bred. The knight's charger was the ancestor of the modern draught horse.

Farming is a conservative industry, or rather way of life. The farmers' reluctance to change time-honoured habits is seen in the way the day's work was organized when ploughs were drawn by horses. The details of

the ploughman's life have been documented by George Ewart Evans who interviewed the old men who had worked on farms during the early years of this century. Although they worked with horses these ploughmen very often followed the same centuries-old routine which had been used with oxen. According to George Ewart Evans' informants, the men were out of bed by 4 o'clock and had fed their horses by 4.30. This early start was necessary so that the horses had time to digest before they started work at 6.30, or 7 o'clock in the winter. Ploughing continued all morning, with a rest for a few minutes every hour, and the horses were returned to the stables at 2.30.

In places where the old system prevailed, the fields stood empty all afternoon but the ploughman's day was not at an end. The horses had to be fed and groomed, and the men were not free until early evening. It was a long day and a hard life, the essence of which has been caught in Thomas Gray's *Elegy written in a country churchyard*:

'The ploughman homeward plods his weary way
And leaves the world to darkness and to me.'

A plough horse received 6·5 kilograms (14 lb) of food every day, and the composition of its diet depended largely on what feed crops were grown locally. It might receive a mixture of beans and corn, or maize. Root crops such as carrots and beet were used instead of cereals in some places. A good supply of chaff was available to add bulk to the feed and make digestion more efficient.

The old horseman was extremely proud and jealous of the appearance of his charges, and each man had his own recipe for producing a shiny coat. Either bryony root or something special like tansy leaves was added to the feed or the coat was treated with paraffin or some other substance. The result was that animals were turned out for their everyday work in a condition resembling the shining, resplendent animals seen in

Left: Cattle on the open ranges of North America are managed by mounted cowboys. While automobiles and planes replace horses in some respects, they are still used in rugged terrain.

Below: A pair of Clydesdale horses ploughing. Clydesdales have longer legs than Shires and work faster. They have feathers only on the back of their legs. Horses have been coming back into favour for farm work, especially for light work.

Above: This Belgian horse is drawing a light roller. The roller is equipped with wooden shafts which are attached to the saddle to keep the roller balanced. The strain is taken by chains which from the shafts to the hames, on the collar.

Right: A pair of American horses draw a harrow to break up clods of soil. Shafts are not needed, as they are with a roller which needs balancing if the rider is not to be thrown or as with a cart which must not run down the horse when it stops.

the show ring. The pride extended to his work. Ploughing was more than turning the soil to break it up and destroy the weeds. It was a craft that could be perfected only by years of experience. When several teams worked together, the apprentice ploughman worked immediately behind the head ploughman and was followed by other experienced men who could cover his mistakes.

The aim of the ploughman was to achieve a field of perfectly parallel furrows. Any deviation remained, etched in the surface of the fields for all passers-by to see and comment on. But because the furrows had to be evenly spaced to take the nozzles of the seed drill, these high standards were not just vanity.

The heyday of the farm horse was the late 18th century and 19th century. By the 20th century, tractors were being introduced. The first appeared in England in 1903, they became widespread after World War I and dominant after World War II. There was a period of transition when horses were used to plough the headlands after a tractor had ploughed the main furrows. Some farms have retained their horses, partly out of sentiment, and the horse as prime mover has become more attractive with the upsurge of fuel oil costs. However, horse ploughing is labour-intensive and is never likely to find favour on the new-style 'prairie farms' where crops extend unbroken hectare after hectare.

The heavy horse or draught horse used on farms is a solidly built, broad-beamed animal of which there are a number of breeds. Many regions of Europe produced heavy horses specially suited to local conditions. This is reflected in their names: the Murakoz comes from the Mure district of Hungary, the Rhineland and Schleswig from Germany and the Ardennes from Belgium. France is the home of the Ardennais, Auxois, Breton and Percheron. The last comes from the Perche region and has strong hoofs for working on rough pavé roads. From Britain, comes the Clydesdale of the Clyde Valley, the Suffolk Punch and, perhaps the most famous, the Shire from the English Midlands. The Shire is the largest horse and

it is slow moving but stamina and willingness are the virtues needed on the heavy soil of its native country. The Cleveland Bay of Yorkshire is lighter, first used as a packhorse and later as a coach horse.

While the horse was a latecomer as a draught animal, it has a long history as the farmer's personal vehicle, carrying him as he goes about his business. On stock farms where herds of cattle and sheep wander over wide tracts of countryside, the horse has proved invaluable. Mounted stockmen have not been so important in the crowded lands of Europe, although the mounted *czikos* (cowboys of Hungary) and the *guardians* of the Camargue are exceptions. In the ranges of the new lands settled by Europeans, stock farming has developed on a large scale with the use of horses. The horse is basic equipment to the sheep herding stockmen of Australia, New Zealand and the Falkland Islands, to the cattle-owning gauchos of South America and, most famous of all, the cowboys of North America. As a vehicle, the horse has some advantages over motor transport. It can cope with rough ground and it is less likely to scare the stock. Moreover, riding does not require constant attention and the stockman is free to keep watch on his charges. Indeed, a well-trained horse knows its job as well as a sheepdog.

Cowboys have been part of the American scene from the time of the earliest European settlements. Their function was to drive herds of cattle from farm to market (for sale) or seaport (for shipment) but when Americans reached Texas they found and adopted the Mexican ranch system employing *vaqueros*, the Mexican name for cowboys. The cattle on the ranches were Longhorns which could survive hard winters and fatten on poor grazing. The Texas cowboys taught their new skills to farmers of neighbouring States and, after the Civil War, new markets opened in the booming towns in the East. In 1867 stockyards were built at the railway in Abilene, Kansas, and the heyday of the coyboy had arrived. The herds were driven up regular trails from Texas and other states to Abilene and later to Dodge City where they were freighted east.

The other highpoint of the cowboy's year was the round-up, when the cattle, which had been scattered on the range, were sought out and gathered together, literally for stocktaking! The cattle were counted and calves were branded with the ranch's mark.

The ranch system depended on the open range where cattle lived almost wild and the cowboys' world began to close in on them in the 1880's. Barbed wire fences cut up the country and sheep farmers moved in. The railways expanded to cut out the need for trail driving, cold winters destroyed the cattle and finally there was a slump in prices. Cowboys still exist and they still ride horses but motor vehicles and helicopters are increasingly used.

The horses used by cowboys were usually either mustangs, captured from herds which lived wild in North America since they escaped from the Spanish conquistadores, or the Quarter Horse. The latter originated in Virginia 300 years ago and is so named

Right: The mounted sheep-herder of the United States is a nomad. Each year he moves his flock of 1,000 or more sheep up to 500 kilometres from their winter quarters to higher summer pastures. Many of the sheep-herders are of Basque descent and, with only their dogs for company, they spend weeks at a time living in covered wagons.

34

because it was regularly raced over a quarter mile. The mustang's great advantage is its hardiness and ability to thrive on poor grazing, whereas the Quarter Horse is noted for 'cow-sense' and manoeuvrability which make it valuable in the cattle round-up. The Canadians have refined the quarter horse into the Cutting Horse which is much used in rodeos. The Australian equivalent is the Waler, developed in New South Wales. It is a mixture of Arab and Thoroughbred and is famed for its stamina.

Whereas the horse was a comparative newcomer to man's stable of domestic animals, the dog is the oldest of them all. There seems to be no doubt now that its ancestor is the wolf. Domestication could have occurred as early as 10,000 years ago but it is difficult to tell the difference between bones of wild and the original domestic dogs. The distinguishing features of modern dogs, as compared with the old are the upturned tail and the out-turned elbows which cause the prints of the hindfeet to be placed beside rather than over those of the forefeet. The assumption is that wild dogs came into human encampments to scavenge, as they still do today. They also accompanied human hunting parties and the first use of dogs was to help in hunts, flushing and running down prey which was shared with their human companions, but dogs, like foxes, were kept for the pot.

Dogs which lived in and around camps would soon have assumed the role of guards and when man started to keep herds of cattle or sheep, his dogs would naturally guard the livestock, too. Powerfully built dogs detected and dealt with rustlers, both human and animal. These dogs developed into such modern breeds as the Alsatian or German Shepherd, the breed which most resembles the ancestral wolf. The Old English sheepdog which is as woolly as its charges is another 'guard' type of sheepdog.

It must have taken some skill and patience to teach these dogs to guard rather than to eat sheep. The enormous numbers of sheep killed and menaced by dogs each year is evidence that the hunting trait has never been bred out of dogs. Even greater skill was needed to train dogs to herd sheep or cattle. The training of a sheepdog goes well beyond the teaching of tricks and obedience sufficient for a housedog. The sheepdog has to retain independence of action and initiative within a general framework of obedience. The dog has to understand what it is doing and anticipate its master's wishes. There are plenty of anecdotes which demonstrate the almost uncanny intelligence of sheepdogs. There are, for instance, numerous stories of dogs which attracted the attention of the shepherd and led him to a sheep in some sort of trouble.

There are several breeds of dog used for herding rather than guarding. They are small, active and run with a characteristic lope which enables them to run to and fro all day. The common, 'ordinary' sheepdog the world over is the Border collie. Easily recognized, it is not standardized as are the more showy breeds. Typically it is black with white collar and tail tip, has slender legs and carries the tail low. The Shetland sheepdog or Sheltie is essentially a miniature collie which has long been used in the Shetland Isles. The Maltese is a very old breed and is even smaller than the Sheltie. The Kennel Club of Great Britain recognizes several more sheepdogs, such as the Anatolian and Maremma (of Italy) sheepdogs and the

Above left: A pair, or yoke, of oxen pulling a plough on a French farm. The wooden yoke is attached to the horns by leather straps rather than resting on the withers. It is padded with sheepskins. Oxen are still used in Europe; they need less care than horses and survive on poor grazing.

Above: These Portuguese longhorned oxen wear a more elaborate harness. The yoke is carved and the shaft can be seen attached in the middle. Note the muzzles on the oxen.

Australian Kelpy and there are some non-recognized breeds. Lack of recognition does not imply that the the breed is insignificant, however. Even the Border collie is not recognized as a showbreed because it is a working dog and is not bred for showing.

An unusual sheepdog type of breed is the Corgi. Popularized in Britain as a town pet and a royal favourite, the Corgi was developed as a cattle herder. Its short legs would seem to render it quite useless for any strenuous activity. The Corgi's function is to follow the herd of cattle, not a fast-moving procession, and keep the laggards moving by nipping their legs. Its low stature helps the corgi to avoid being kicked. Other cattle dogs include the Rottweiler, a dog famous for its intelligence and popular as a police dog and as a guide-dog for the blind, the Australian cattle dog, the Kerry Blue of Ireland and the Schnauzer of Germany.

The farm is often the home of another group of dogs, the terriers. Their name is derived from the French *terre* (ground) and these dogs are used for flushing foxes or badgers from their underground burrows. Consequently, terriers are usually small animals with an aggressiveness that is out of proportion to their size. On the farm, terriers are often used as watchdogs; their frenzied bark perhaps being a greater deterrent than their bite. The Irish terrier, in particular, has a great reputation as a courageous watchdog.

Another use for terriers is to kill rats and mice and the Yorkshire terrier was bred for the purpose. More often rodents are the responsibility of the farm cats. The farm cat must be the least domesticated of all domestic animals. It is not trained to do anything and it provides no useful product. Only its natural hunting behaviour is of any use to the farmer, who does not have to corral it or supervise its breeding. The most it gets is a plate of food and many farm cats are so wild that they will not allow themselves to be stroked.

In the farm cat we see the earliest stage of domestication, a mutual tolerance and exploitation between animal and Man. It seems likely that cats took the initiative in the domestication process by coming into human settlements to scavenge or hunt. The Azande tribe of the Sudan let cafer cats (the ancestor of the domestic cat) gather in their villages to kill rats but they make no attempt to domesticate them. The behaviour of the farm cat differs from its wild ancestor in two important ways. It tolerates the nearness of human beings and is in turn tolerated because it has learned not to attack poultry.

Breeding for Bulk

Farming provides the human race with food. The farmer either grows plant crops which he sells for human consumption or which he feeds to animals which then provide meat or milk. It is most efficient for us to eat plants direct without the intervening animal stage but there are several reasons for eating meat rather than vegetables. Animals are a means of storing food – they are walking larders. They can also eat plant food which is not palatable or digestible by human beings. Finally, for most people, meat is eaten because it tastes nice. Primitive tribes will go to the trouble of hunting large animals even when they can make an easier living by gathering plants and insects.

The prime reason for the domestication of meat-producing animals is their ability to convert inedible plants into edible flesh. Man is unable to digest cellulose, the substance which makes up the bulk of plant tissues. Plant tissues are made up of tiny units called cells. The walls of these cells are made of cellulose and human beings lack the necessary digestive enzyme for breaking down these cell walls and setting free the protoplasm within. In consequence, we derive little nutrition from eating grass shoots or the leaves of plants. To take advantage of the energy

available in the huge areas of productive grasslands that cover many parts of the world, human beings have exploited those animals which can digest cellulose. The most important of these are the hoofed animals. They are ideal for domestication because of their large bulk and their habit of living in herds. Among the hoofed animals, the most efficient converters of plant food are the ruminants, which include cattle, sheep and goats.

Ruminant animals have four stomachs which are designed for the processing of large quantities of coarse plant food. The actual digestion of the cellulose is carried out by bacteria and single-celled protozoons in the stomachs and these microscopic animals are then digested in turn and absorbed into the animal's body, along with the protoplasm from inside the plants' tissue cells.

The ruminants spend a large part of their time eating. Compare, for instance, a cow feeding at a bale of hay with a dog or cat bolting its bowl of meat. When cows are feeding they sweep sheaves of grass into their mouth with a curling action of the long tongue and the stems are sheared off as the tongue pulls them over the incisor teeth. Sheep and goats have short tongues and

Left: Farm animals convert grass or other vegetable food into protein and fat which can be eaten by human beings. This Brown Swiss cow belongs to one of the oldest breeds. Originally the breed was kept for its meat and for work but when feeding was improved in the 19th century, it also became a dairy animal.

Right: The Hereford breed started as a work animal but it has become one of the world's most famous beef producers. It replaced the Texas Longhorn in North America and thrives in hot countries. This bull shows the characteristic red body and the white face which, together with the deep body, are the hallmarks of the Hereford.

Above: The long-haired, handle-bar-horned Highland cattle are a familiar sight in the mountain regions of Scotland and the breed has been exported to America, Australia and South Africa. These cattle are extremely hardy and have a dense undercoat which is exposed in summer when the outer coat is shed.

they feed by nipping stems and leaves between the incisor teeth in the lower jaw and the hard pad on the upper jaw (ruminants lack the upper incisors). The grass is swallowed without much chewing and is stored in the first of the stomachs, called the rumen or paunch. Here digestion of cellulose takes place. The food is stored in the rumen until the meal is finished and the ruminant – the cow, goat or sheep – retires to a quiet place where it can digest in peace.

We see herds of cattle lying in a shady corner of the field with their jaws working rhythmically. They are chewing the cud, or ruminating. Wads of food are brought up into the mouth and given a second, very thorough, chewing. Afterwards, the food is swallowed again and it passes to the other stomachs, to the reticulum and omasum where it receives another crushing and then to the abomasum. The abomasum is the equivalent of our single stomach and is the place where the digested food is absorbed into the blood stream.

Other hoofed animals can digest cellulose but they are not so efficient as the true ruminants. The pigs have a system of stomachs rather like those of the ruminants but horses have a simple system and cellulose is digested in the lower part of the intestine. Consequently horses need to eat more food because it is not digested thoroughly.

Farm animals have rarely been kept for a single purpose. We have already seen that cattle were used as draught animals and slaughtered when past their prime. They then provided meat and leather and, no doubt, their bones were used to make glue. Hardly a

part of the animal would have been wasted but nowadays there is a trend for specialization in farms and farm animals. Cattle are kept for meat or for milk, and special breeds have been developed for each purpose. Similarly sheep are kept and bred for meat or wool. There are breeds, however, which serve both purposes but on modern, intensive farms, operations are such that the emphasis is often on one product.

It is difficult to reconstruct the appearance of the original food-producing farm animals. We have to rely mainly on old pictures and descriptions but we do know something of the aurochs, the ancestor of modern cattle. This was a massive animal. The bull stood 2 metres (6·5 feet) at the withers and had huge curving horns. Aurochs lived in the forests of Europe and Asia and they were frequently captured and domesticated. Then, as domestic herds were built up, the wild aurochs were hunted because they competed with the farm animal. The last aurochs died in a Polish park in 1627.

In the 1920's and 1930's, attempts were made to breed back to the original aurochs by crossing a number of modern breeds. At Munich Zoo, Germany, Heinz Heck crossed Hungarian, Podolean, Highland, Friesian, Corsican and alpine cattle, and produced an animal which not only had the appearance of an aurochs but had the original wild character and agility. Another 'aurochs' was bred at Berlin Zoo by Lutz Heck by mingling Corsican, Camargue, Spanish fighting cattle and British park cattle.

Domestication of cattle started 8,000 years ago, after sheep and goats, and cattle are now the most common, as well as the most bulky, farm animals. At first the size of cattle rapidly diminished because, it is thought, the first farmers found small animals easier to handle. There is, however, the alternative theory that the first domestic cattle became smaller simply because they were kept in pens or were hobbled so that they could not move about freely in search of food and were half starved. Whichever is correct, there was an initial trend for smaller cattle which was reversed as husbandry techniques improved and farmers obviously sought to produce as much meat from their animals as possible.

It should not be forgotten that only during the last two centuries has the main problem of stock-farming been overcome. This is what to do with the animals in winter. As autumn progresses, grazing becomes progressively sparser. Unless the animals receive additional food in the form of root crops, hay or silage, they lose condition and may die. Before the introduction of supplementary feed crops, it was the practice to slaughter the majority of the stock. The favoured survivors were not large, bulky animals but those that could subsist on the slenderest diet. Even so, in a severe winter, those that lived had to be literally carried out to the spring pastures.

By Roman times breeds of cattle had appeared with the character of beef animals. They had short, stout limbs and the heaviest weight of meat was concentrated around the hindquarters.

Roman cattle are still with us. They were carried across Europe in the wake of the legions and often turned wild when Roman civilization was shattered by barbarian invasions. In Britain, descendants of these cattle roamed free and were hunted until 300 years ago. During the reign of the Plantagenet kings, parks were set up in England as hunting preserves for the nobles. Herds of wild cattle were enclosed with other beasts of the chase and some still survive, as at Chillingham and Chartley. In modern times these 'park cattle' have been bred into other lines to establish the White Park breed of beef cattle.

After the collapse of the Roman government, Britain was invaded by the Germanic tribes we now know as the Anglo-Saxons. They brought their own red cattle, which we have already seen to have been held very valuable. The importance of cattle in the old rural economies is seen in the very name. 'Cattle' comes from the same Latin word *capitale* as our words chattel and capital; all mean 'property'.

When the Normans conquered the Anglo-Saxons and dominated the land, there was a significant change

Above: A Charolais bull and cow. This breed is descended from cattle brought into France by the Romans.

Below: An idyllic scene on an Oregon farm with Shorthorn cattle and sheep grazing on the same pasture. Like other famous breeds, Shorthorns were developed in Britain.

in the naming of cattle and other farm animals. The results are still to be seen in our everyday language. The French-speaking Norman conquerors talked of *boeufs*, *moutons* and *porcs*. They ate the meat which we now describe as beef, mutton and pork. The conquered English tended the animals, which they knew by the names of cattle, sheep and pigs or swine.

Over the course of centuries, more breeds have been brought into Britain. The Danes, who settled in northern England and southern Scotland, brought dun coloured, hornless cattle. Then, from the 16th to 18th centuries, Dutch breeds with patchwork coats of black or red and white were brought over the North Sea. The island became a melting pot for cattle and recent years have seen introductions of French Limousin and Charolais breeds, the Dutch Meuse-Rhine-Ijssel and the Italian Chianina.

The new breeds have been re-exported around the world, also as a continuing process. When Europeans explored the new lands overseas they found vast expanses of grasslands and settlers poured onto these with their herds and flocks. Cattle were taken to the pampas of South America, the prairies and plains of North America, the South African veldt and the ranges of Australia. Climate was often different from

that in native Europe and the settlers had to find breeds which could thrive in the new conditions.

The most famous of these transplanted cattle must be the Texas Longhorn which has thundered across innumerable cinema screens. The Texas Longhorn was developed from the Warwick Longhorn which is now rare, numbering only 200 beasts. It flourished in the grasslands of south-west United States because it could survive the long dry summers and its lanky, athletic build enabled it to forage for scanty grazing over large areas. As a hardy animal, the Texas Longhorn required the minimum of care and could be allowed to roam the open range.

After the Civil War, the central prairies were rapidly stripped of their bison herds. This left the grasslands empty and the space was filled with the Texas Longhorn. It remained as the dominant breed, and saw the setting-up of the cowboy culture and myth, until the open plains were fenced and ploughed. As the land was tamed, fancy, higher-yielding breeds could be brought in and the Texas Longhorn dwindled and nearly died out.

Luckily, some Texas Longhorns were preserved and their fortunes have taken a new turn. The international oil crisis and the move to ecological

awareness has brought the breed back into favour. Rising prices of fuel and oil-based fertilizers and pesticides have pushed up the cost of grain feeds and labour has become ever more expensive, so farmers have looked for cattle which can thrive on poor feed, are resistant to attack by pests and need little attention. The Texan Longhorn fits the bill and some of its other qualities, such as easy calving and the large number of calves produced per cow, are being introduced to other breeds by cross-breeding.

Of the more famous beef breeds which may be mentioned here, the white-headed Hereford, the Highland with its shaggy coat and long horns, and the black Aberdeen Angus are seen in many parts of the world. A trend in North America is to cross the zebu or Brahman cattle with European breeds. The zebu is recognized by the hump on its shoulders and it survives well in hot, dry countries where grazing is poor. Hence, zebus have been crossed with Shorthorns to make the Santa Gertrudis, with Shorthorns and Herefords to make the Beefmaster, with Aberdeen Angus to make Brangus and with Charolais to make Charbray.

The Santa Gertrudis was developed in Texas because the Shorthorns brought in to replace the Texas Longhorns could not survive drought. The breed has now spread to other dry parts of the American continent, to Australia and to South Africa. In Australia a tough, heat and disease-resistant breed, the Droughtmaster, has been bred from Brahman and Shorthorn. A novel breed from America is the Beefalo, a mixture of Hereford, Charolais and the bison (or buffalo). Because the bison is a separate species of cattle-like animal the original offspring were sterile, as the mule is a sterile hybrid of horse and donkey, but a fertile strain was produced in 1960.

Domestic sheep are nearly as numerous in the world as cattle but their smaller size lessens their importance. The first sheep were kept not for their meat or wool but for their milk. However, it is difficult to believe that the people who first kept sheep did not also appreciate the value of their meat and fleeces. The hair of most mammals is made up of two types: a short fine underfur and long coarse guard hairs which overlie the underfur. The wool of sheep is a very exaggerated underfur and the aim of woolbreeders is to increase the proportion of wool to guard hair.

In primitive breeds, such as Soay sheep and Shetland sheep, the wool moults naturally each spring and falls out in sheets. We must presume that the first

shepherds collected this wool and used it as a sort of felt or padding, but they may have already been weaving vegetable fibres and so easily realized the potential of sheep's wool. Three thousand years ago there were sheep with thick fleeces which had to be sheared but even now the primitive Soays and Shetlands have their wool plucked.

In mediaeval England, sheep replaced cattle as the mainstay of agriculture. The soft, lush countryside in the south of the country was ideal for sheep and sheep farming became the basis of the country's prosperity. This economic importance is reflected in the name given to the symbolic seat of the Lord Chancellor in the House of Lords – the Woolsack. The organization of the wool industry laid the foundations of capitalism in Britain and saw the rise of the affluent mercantile class. Wool penetrated all levels of society and in everyday English we speak of 'teasing', 'spinning a yarn' and 'homespun', and unmarried women are still called spinsters.

Raw wool for weaving was exported to Flanders and Italy but this was short-circuited where possible by persuading Flemish weavers to settle in England. The English did not have a monopoly of the wool market. The native breeds of the Lincoln, Cotswold, Romney and Southdown had coarse wool which was challenged by the Merino, a fine-woolled breed living in Spain.

The history of the Merino goes back over 2,000 years to a fine-woolled sheep especially bred in the

Above: Cheviot sheep spread up through Scotland from the Border country at the end of the 18th century. The Cheviot produces a fine fleece but it is hardy enough to live in the harsh conditions of mountainous country.

Left: A flock of sheep, ewes and their lambs, in Western Australia. Australian sheep, mainly Merinos, produce one third of the world's wool. In 1970, the country contained over 180 million sheep. Some are kept on huge farms or 'stations'.

Near East and carried westwards with the Phoenicians and Romans to Spain. Here the Moors set up a wool industry and later the Spaniards jealously guarded a monopoly on Merino wool. They could not, however, help a few sheep being spirited away, any more than the Chinese could prevent the pilfering of their precious silkworms.

Merinos reached England by devious routes but in 1792, George III ('Farmer George' was his nickname) imported 40 direct from Spain. Under Royal patronage, the merinos were popular for a while and were bred into native varieties, but they did not flourish in the cold, wet British weather. The true flowering of the breed came with the opening of the ranges in new lands. Merinos, and the French Rambouillets which

were bred from them, have been reared in huge numbers in the western United States, in Argentina, South Africa and USSR, but the main base of the Merino is in Australia and New Zealand. The Tasmanian Merino has no equal in the fineness of its wool and the number of wool fibres is five times greater per unit area of skin than in any other breed. Nowadays, Merinos are often crossed with other breeds. The Corriedale of New Zealand and Australia is Merino crossed with Lincoln and Leicester; the Columbia of the United States comes from Rambouillet and Lincoln and is farmed for meat as well as wool.

The second challenge to the lowland sheep of England came from their highland neighbours. Welsh Mountain, Swaledale, Cheviot and Scottish Blackface – the 'hill sheep' – tolerate harsh climate and poor grazing on mountain and moor, so much so that a scattering of shaggy sheep is an essential part of the rain swept scenery of rocks and heather. Cheviot and Blackface are the two most important hill breeds and they came to prominence in the 18th century. After the Jacobite Rebellions, the social structure of the Scottish Highlands began to change and thousands emigrated overseas. The exodus was aided by sheep.

Traditionally the Highlanders kept a few sheep which they herded by day and locked up at night in wolf-proof huts. Then flocks of sheep were brought up from the south. White-faced Cheviots came from the Border hills and Blackfaces, then known as

Lintons, came from the Pennines. These sheep are allowed to roam the open country, as they can survive the winter without extra feeding, and they became almost wild.

Whereas 'lamb' is a term of endearment, the word 'pig', if applied to a human, is a positive insult. This could be because of the bad reputation that pigs have. Pigs, or hogs or swine, are said to be dirty but this is forced on them by the practice of keeping them in cramped sties where they cannot help but foul themselves. Experts on the behaviour of animals have stated that pigs are, in fact, the cleanest animals on the farm. If given the opportunity they make an effort not to foul their bedding or food. Pigs are prone to get fouled because they like to wallow in mud. They share this behaviour with cattle and, as in the words of one popular song, the function is 'for cooling the blood'. On hot days, pigs try to keep cool by moistening their bodies. If there is a puddle available they flop into it and wriggle around to get a plastering of wet mud. On dry ground they root with their snouts to dig a shallow trench and lie with their bodies pressed against the cool sub-soil.

Another feature of pigs, easily overlooked in the sty, is their intelligence. George Orwell chose pigs well as the animals which were 'more equal than others' in *Animal Farm*. Some people have taught pigs to do tricks as easily as dogs and in places there are 'working pigs' which almost qualify the pigs for a place in the preceding chapter.

The most famous working pigs are those used for hunting truffles. A truffle is a fungus which grows several centimetres underground. Very unprepossessing in appearance, truffles are prized by gourmets and can fetch prices of £200 per kilogram. They would be quite impossible to find, except by laborious digging through tonnes of soil, if it were not for their aroma being detectable by the delicate noses of animals.

The truffle industry is centred in the Périgord region of France and pigs or dogs are employed to sniff out the valuable fungi. Dogs have the advantage of being portable – a terrier fits better into the boot of a car than a solid porker. A second advantage of the dog is that it does not eat truffles, whereas the pig competes with its keepers. The pig, however, has the better nose. A dog can detect a truffle only if it is ripe, so it has to be taken around the truffle ground every day, whereas the pig seeks out developing fungi and need be taken round only once a week.

Perhaps no great intelligence is needed to find truffles – only a super-sensitive nose – but pigs have competed with dogs in other areas. In Mediaeval England, the inhabitants of the New Forest, a royal hunting forest, were forbidden to keep dogs large enough to be used in hunting and retrieving. So they

Above: Pigs do not need a large area for pasturage as they are scavengers and can be given freedom to search for their own food around the farm.

Above left: A sow sits contentedly in a farmyard puddle. Pigs are more intelligent than most other farm animals. They are also much more solitary.

used pigs instead. There is a record of a pig, called Slut, who was trained as a 'bird-pig' in the 19th century. She would find, point and retrieve partridges, pheasants, snipe and rabbits as well as the best dog and showed every excitement when taken out with a gun.

Truffle-hunting and retrieving are unusual uses for a pig, as is its use in pulling carts. The main reason for pig-keeping is the provision of meat. The domestication of the pig started some 5,000 years ago, when the European wild pig was tamed. Normally one of the fiercest of wild animals, pigs submitted to domestication readily.

There is an important difference between the domestication of pigs, on the one hand, and cattle, sheep and goats, on the other. The latter three are ruminating animals and are easily herded. They could be brought under control by nomadic tribes. Pigs, while docile, do not submit easily to being driven in herds. Consequently pig farming could only start when people started to live in permanent settlements.

There are two traditional methods of farming pigs.

They can be confined in the sty or they can be allowed to roam free. The feeding habits of pigs differ from the ruminant sheep, goats and cattle in being extremely liberal. They can be kept on any scraps or cheap foods like potatoes. They do not disdain flesh and are sometimes fed on offal. It is said that the best way for a murderer to dispose of his victim's body is to leave it in a pig-sty. Nothing will remain. Be that as it may, pigs are easy to keep. As they do not require a large expanse of grazing, they were ideal animals for country people to keep behind their cottages, converting otherwise worthless scraps into valuable meat and fat.

The alternative way of keeping pigs is to let them roam in the forest, at least for part of the year. In the autumn, the pigs used to be turned out to feed on fallen acorns and beech mast, the right to do so being called pannage.

Pig farming has always been popular in Europe and has also been very important in China but pigs are not eaten in the Near East and are considered unclean in both Jewish and Moslem religions. There are several suggestions as to why there should be this attitude towards pigs. The most widely held explanation is that pigs harbour tapeworms and other parasites in their flesh. If pork is not properly cooked these are transmitted to humans. This is the reason why pork and other pig meat has to be cured before sale.

49

Perhaps a better explanation lies in the nature of pig farming. As already mentioned, pigs are kept by settled people and nomadic tribes traditionally feel superior to farmers, an attitude still held by the Bedouin Arabs. They would consequently feel it beneath their dignity to eat farmers' animals and this attitude has become enshrined in the religion of Hebrew pastoralists and their spiritual descendants.

In Europe, pigs were sacred to the heathen gods. The Norse god and goddess Frey and Freya kept two pigs, Gullinbursti (Golden bristles) and Hildisvin (Battlepig). Warriors carried boar's head standards or had boar emblems on their helmets to show they were under the protection of these gods. The boar was sacrificed at the midwinter festival of Yule, a custom which is echoed in the later ceremony of the boar's head at Christmas.

The keeping of pigs did not reach the scale of cattle or sheep farming until the age of the factory farm when pigs could be raised intensively in indoor pens under controlled conditions. A great feature of pigs is their productivity. A litter of pigs numbers nine, compared with a single calf and two or three lambs. Each sow produces more than one litter a year. So a 'pig factory' with a standing stock of 12,000 animals can send 18,000 a year to the market, where, say the butchers, everything can be marketed 'except the squeal'.

The breeding of pigs developed, as with other farm animals, in the 18th and 19th centuries. Chinese pigs, which are derived from a species different from the European wild boar, were imported and interbred with native pigs. An advantage gained from the Chinese blood is early maturity. The Berkshire is a British breed with a large Chinese ancestry, from which it gets its broad, compact body and dished face. Berkshires have been exported to North America and Australia. In the United States, it was used to make a new breed in Warren County, Ohio. First called 'Warren County hogs' the breed was eventually christened the Poland China and is now the most important pig in the United States.

Another British export is the Tamworth which has a striking gold-red colour. As it does not burn so readily under a hot sun as a white pig, it has been exported to Australasia and Asia. The Landrace has been imported to Britain, mainly from Sweden. It is a white pig with floppy ears. Landrace merely means 'native breed', so Danish Landrace is the Danish variety of the breed. Landrace pigs come from Northwest Europe, particularly Scandinavia, and they have been selected for bacon production by the development of long slender bodies. The Duroc-Jersey is a 19th century breed which is widely farmed in North and South America, and is suitably based on pigs descended from those brought over by Christopher Columbus in the fifteenth century.

Above: Landrace pigs have lop-ears and long, white bodies. The long body is specially designed to maximize bacon production but the most highly-developed strains produce poor meat and are susceptible to disease and poor conditions.

Facing page: Young pigs are given freedom to run about together in a large pen. When small they are allowed to squeeze between the bars of their mother's pen and roam free.

Below: Essex Saddleback pigs are named after the white belt over the shoulders which contrasts with the black of the rest of the body. The Saddleback is a hardy breed which lives outside.

Dairy Animals

There is the famous story of the townchild, on a visit to a farm, who disdainfully exclaimed: 'We get our milk from nice clean bottles, not dirty old cows'. The milk bottle, the packet of butter and the slab of cheese are so much a part of our everyday lives, on sale in hygienic, neatly packed portions, that we are liable to forget that they came from 'dirty old cows'.

Left: An inquisitive goat peers out from the shade of ruins on Crete. Goats are important farm animals in warm, dry parts of the world as they are easy to keep in barren areas.

Below: Sheep were first kept as dairy animals but today they are usually kept to provide meat and wool.

Dairy products have been important in human diet where and whenever farm animals have been kept. It seems probable that milk was at first only a by-product from animals which were kept mainly for their meat. Milk is produced only after an animal has given birth and farmers can milk their animals either by taking away the young animal or by stimulating the mother to continue production after her offspring have been weaned. Casual milking does not give high yields but at least 5,000 years ago, the Sumerians living in the city of Ur had bred a special dairy cow. Pictures found at archaeological sites show that it was

53

of a Shorthorn variety and not much different from the main milk producers now living in the drier parts of the world.

Milk goes sour very rapidly, particularly in hot weather, and before refrigeration this severely limited its uses. The solution to the problem was to turn milk into non-perishable cheese which can be easily kept and carried. The high food value of cheese made it an excellent provision for travellers. Those masters of the ocean travel, the Vikings, carried cheeses in their longships and their land-bound counterparts, the Mongols of Genghiz Khan, included dried milk in their rations.

Before looking at the animals who give our milk products, let us first examine these products. Milk is a secretion peculiar to mammals. It is used for feeding newborn offspring until they can find their own food. The milk has to supply the baby mammal with all its needs, so it is the most complete of all natural foods. Most of it is water – 87 per cent in cow's milk – and the

remainder is energy-giving and body-building solids: 3·8 per cent fat, 3·4 per cent protein and 4·8 per cent milk sugar. There are also some, but not all, of the vital vitamins needed for good health and minerals such as calcium and phosphorus which are especially necessary for the growth of bones.

Cheese can be described as dehydrated milk. The solids in the milk are coagulated by the addition of rennet, the same substance that is used in making junket, and are turned into curds. The whey that remains is almost pure water. The curds are turned into cheese in a number of ways, each resulting in a different variety.

Butter has been more important in the cooler countries of northern Europe than in the south. It used to be made from the excess milk coming from animals feeding on lush summer grass. The raw material is butterfat and in the traditional way of making butter, the milk was left in a broad, shallow dish for the globules of butterfat to float to the surface as cream. The cream was skimmed off and the remainder – skim milk – fed to the farm animals. Settling and skimming is a very slow process and the milk is liable to go sour. It is now passed through a separator which spins the milk so that the lighter cream is thrown from the heavier 'separated milk'. To turn the cream into butter it is agitated in a churn until the fat globules coalesce into a mass and the remaining fluid – buttermilk – is drained off.

Facing page: Jersey cows have a soft coat of fawn or brown hair and sometimes have white patches. They originated on the island of Jersey, but the breed has been established world-wide. A good cow yields ten times her body weight of milk annually. Guernsey dairy cows have a lower yield.

Below: Although these two goats make a charming sight as they reach up to nibble the leaves of a fruit tree, the habit has led to some places being devastated. Goats will climb trees and completely strip their foliage, and they crop the herbage beneath so close that a desert is created.

Right: A dairy goat is checked by the judge at a goat show. Goats' milk is often used to make cheese, but many people like to drink it in preference to cows' milk because it is more easily digested.

Far right top: The Anglo-Nubian goat is descended from Abyssinian goats and is recognized by its Roman nose and long floppy ears. The hair is short and the colour variable. The Anglo-Nubian produces slightly less milk than other dairy goats, which are of Swiss origin, but the milk is creamier.

Far right below: British Toggenburg goats at rest. Their browsing is opening up an overgrown paddock as they eat back the coarse herbage and brambles. Of the three Swiss breeds, the Toggenburg, Saanen and Alpine, the Toggenburg is the smallest. All have erect ears and a concave face. They form the basis of most milk breeds except the Nubian.

All the domesticated ruminants have been kept for their milk; and it is rather surprising to find that the first use of sheep was to provide milk. Mutton and wool came later. Sheep's milk is still important in many parts of the world. The East Friesland is a milk breed of sheep which comes from the same district as the champion Friesian dairy cow. In England, Cheddar and Wensleydale cheeses were traditionally made from sheep's milk and Roquefort cheese comes from sheep living in the French Alps. The yak of Tibet is another milk producer, rancid yak butter or ghee being an important item of food. However, the oldest dairy animal is the goat which has spent more time under domestication than any other.

The goat is the most successful farm animal in the Near East, Asia and Africa but it has not enjoyed the same success in Europe or the countries colonized by Europeans. However, as goats readily go wild, there are colonies of goats living a natural life in many wild

places and, as Europeans sailed about the world, they left goats on uninhabited islands as a reserve food for shipwrecked mariners. Unfortunately, the goats proceeded to wreak havoc with the native vegetation as they had already done around the shores of the Mediterranean. Nothing escapes the goats' close-cropping teeth and they will even climb trees to browse on the leaves.

In more fertile parts of the world, the goat comes a poor second to the sheep in the quality of its meat and wool and the sheep thrives better on rich grassland. The goat is a browser rather than a grazer, that is it eats leaves of shrubs and trees rather than grass. And as it likes dry, aromatic herbs it can survive up mountains and into deserts beyond the range of other domestic animals.

In the western world and in China, the goat is kept mainly for its milk. It is sometimes called 'the poor man's cow' because, like the pig, it can be maintained

on a small patch of ground with poor quality food. One or two goats can supply milk needed for one family but good management is needed to arrange for milk to be available the year round. Although wild goats survive in the mountainous parts of Britain, the species really belongs to warmer climes and domestic goats cannot be simply turned into a field and left to their own devices if any reasonable yield of milk is expected.

In the West, most goats' milk is turned into cheese but the milk itself has valuable properties. The fat globules are finer than in cows' milk and they are easier to digest by infants and invalids. On the traditional farm, a few goats were often kept for purposes other than milking. On hill farms they were allowed to run with herds of cattle. One explanation for this is that white goats helped the farmer locate a distant herd of black or brown cattle. Goats were also said to prevent the cattle catching the disease known as contagious abortion but the real advantage was thought to be that they would eat plants which would poison the cattle. It is true that goats tend to be fairly resistant to certain poisonous plants but they are certainly not immune to all of them. The suggestion has also been made that goats were allowed to run wild on hill farms because they would easily scale crags to remove the temptingly lush tussocks of grass growing on narrow ledges. Less nimble sheep and

Above: Mechanical milking equipment takes the drudgery out of the daily chore and allows large herds to be managed by a small labour force. Milking by suction machine is more hygienic and faster than hand milking.

cattle would then not be tempted to climb up and get stuck or fall.

Most modern breeds of dairy goat originated in Switzerland or have a large amount of Swiss blood. There are three main Swiss breeds: Saanen goats are cream or white; Toggenberg, the smallest, are brown with stripes of white on face, legs and tail; and Alpine goats vary from white to brown, grey or black. All three have short hair and erect ears. Another Swiss breed, the Schwarzhal, was brought to England by returning Crusaders. Since their arrival in the 14th

century these goats and their descendants have roamed semi-wild in Bagot's Park, in the English county of Staffordshire. Now known as Bagot goats, they have long hair and have a striking coloration of black on head, neck and shoulders and white on the rest of the body.

The Nubian goat is also an important dairy breed. It comes from Nubia, in the north-east of Africa, and the first to reach Europe are said to have been presented to the French Emperor, Napoleon III. The hair is short, the colour varied, the ears are long and drooping and the nose is Roman. The original Nubians were crossed with the old British breeds to form the Anglo-Nubian. This is the main dairy goat in the United States. The yield of milk is less than that of the Swiss goats but it is very rich.

But no matter how valuable the goat is in some parts

of the world, no animal can surpass the cow as a milk producer. The *average* annual yield of a Friesian cow is more than double that of the *best* goats, and more than five times the average goat production of milk. Although grass is the natural food of cattle, milk production is improved if a more balanced diet is given. In New Zealand, where dairy cattle eat only grass, the annual yield per cow is 41 per cent less than that of the average United States yield where extra foodstuffs are given to cattle. Extra food in the form of silage, hay or root crops is particularly necessary where the grazing is poor.

Since the Sumerians developed their dairy cattle many centuries ago, breeds have come and gone. Today there are five major dairy breeds, together with some lesser lights. Compared with the chunky beef cattle, dairy cows have lighter forequarters and broad hips, giving a wedge-shaped appearance.

As with other branches of farming, the major advances were made in the later parts of the 18th century. During this period there were a number of pioneering farmers whose experiments changed the agricultural scene. The Ayrshire, now one of the

Above: A Guernsey cow lying among buttercups is a charming sight but buttercups are mildly poisonous and they crowd out the nutritious grasses and herbs. Guernseys are fawn, often with white markings, and a cream muzzle.

Previous spread: Friesian cows graze and ruminate in the foreground of a perfect rural setting – a much more appropriate setting than the strictly controlled grazing which is the lot of cows on an intensively managed farm.

major dairy breeds, was created virtually on a single farm – that of John Dunlop of Dunlop House, Dunlop in the county of Ayrshire. Not surprisingly these cattle were first called Dunlop cattle. Then, as the breed spread across the county they became known as Ayrshires. There is no record of what blood Mr Dunlop introduced into his cattle. There appears to be Dutch, Jersey and Chillingham ancestry in the Ayrshire which, nowadays is usually brown and white or, more rarely, black and white.

Dutch blood has been introduced into a number of British breeds and the superior of all dairy cattle is the Friesian, known as the Holstein-Friesian or Holstein in North America. Friesians are black and white in varying patterns but the tuft of the tail and lower legs

are always white. The breed was developed a century earlier than the Ayrshire and was brought into Britain during the great agricultural revolution. The record for milk production is 142,332 kilograms delivered during the $17\frac{1}{2}$-year lifetime of a British Friesian called Manningford Faith Jan Graceful.

France has contributed two famous dairy breeds which could be said to be 'naturalized English'. Jerseys and Guernseys come from the islands of these names. The Jersey, with its fawn to dark brown coat sometimes broken with white, resembles cattle in nearby Normandy and Brittany but severe import regulations have kept it separate for two centuries. The Guernsey, fawn like the Jersey but with a cream muzzle and white tail tuft, is the older breed. Two

groups of Norman monks settled on the island before the conquest of England. Each brought their own cows which combined to make the Guernsey.

The fifth of the important dairy cows is the Brown Swiss. Dairying is important in the alpine regions where cattle, sheep and goats are driven to high pastures in the summer and brought down in winter to graze on snow-free ground or to be fed indoors on hay. The Brown Swiss is one of the oldest breeds of cattle and started as a beef and draught animal. When root crops and hay became available in the 19th century, milk production increased and improved cheese manufacturing created a new market.

The Brown Swiss is now becoming a dual purpose animal, giving both milk and meat. Dairy animals have always ended in the slaughterhouse but there are several breeds which are bred with both markets in mind. These include the Devon, the Dexter of Ireland, and the Meuse-Rhine-Ijssel of the Netherlands. Even the Friesian, the ultimate of dairy cows, is bred as a dual purpose animal in its native country and the Shorthorn is separated into two strains, the beef Shorthorn and the dairy Shorthorn.

63

Barnyard Birds

Poultry is the term used for domesticated birds which are kept for their meat and eggs. This includes chickens, turkeys, ducks, geese, guineafowl and pigeons. Of these, the chickens are by far the most important and, in advanced countries, chicken farming has become a large industry.

The domestic chicken or fowl is descended from the red jungle fowl which lives in the forests of Asia, from India through Malaysia and Indo-China to southern China. Like the wild forebears of other domestic animals, jungle fowl have been extensively hunted for centuries. They have survived only because they are extremely shy and difficult to find in dense vegetation.

The earliest history of domestic chickens is not well-known. There were domestic chickens in India

Left: Domestic chickens have been kept for a variety of reasons, including fortune-telling, cock-fighting, egg-laying and fostering the young of other birds. The White Leghorn is the world's most popular laying breed. This cockerel displays the red comb and wattles which he uses to display his superiority to his rivals.

Right: A white Emden goose hardly differs from its wild grey-lag ancestor, except in colour and bulk. Goose feathers, for quill pens, the flights of arrows and stuffing quilts, were once a very important farm product.

Above: Part of a large flock of White turkey hens which will end up on the table. The huge prize turkey, the pride of the poulterer's shop, is fast disappearing because smaller, rapidly-marketed birds suit modern domestic conditions.

Right: The impressive 'strutting' display of a cock turkey attracts the hens. He paces slowly to and fro with tail fanned, body feathers puffed out and wings trailing. The snood on top of the beak elongates and hangs down and, as the display proceeds, the caruncles change from red to blue and white. Males threaten each other with a similar display except that when this happens the body feathers are sleeked down.

four thousand years ago and they had reached China and Egypt by 1400 BC. There is a painting of a cock in the tomb of Tutankhamen. It seems that the first chickens were not farm animals. They were probably eaten but their main use was in the cruel sport of cock-fighting, in which two cocks were set against each other in a fight often to the death. Chickens were also used in religious sacrifices and for prophesying the future. They were good for sacrificing because they were cheaper than sheep, goats or cattle. The Romans foretold the omens by placing chickens in a cage with some food. If they ate greedily, the omens were good; if they showed little interest in the food, they were bad. Obviously, this method is open to abuse. The chickens could be starved or force-fed to produce the right answer.

As to the chicken's arrival in the farmyard, we know from the writings of the Greek playwrite Aristophanes that the Athenians kept chickens in the fourth century BC. Every household, however poor, kept chickens for their eggs. This has been the advantage of 'keeping chickens' through the ages. They are much smaller than other domestic animals and so can be kept in a very small space and fed on very little food, or allowed to forage for themselves. Even in cities there was room for people to keep chickens.

We also know that chicken farming was important to the Ancient Greeks because a law against 'luxury spending' forbad the eating of chickens which had been fattened by force-feeding and only one unfattened chicken could be served at a meal. The Greeks also invented the capon, the castrated cockerel, which fattens well. Romans continued to develop chicken farming. In a book on the subject, the author recommends placing the chicken house near the kitchen so that the smoke would kill lice. It was considered that red or brown hens with black wings and tail were the best layers. White chickens were not popular because they are easily spotted by birds of prey.

Despite the occurrence of white and other colour varieties, the common domestic chicken did not differ much from its wild ancestors except in size and weight. The basic greenish-black, brown and russet

coloration of the cockerel, and drabber hen, was retained. For all their importance to household economy, chickens did not receive much attention from agriculturalists. Chicken-keeping was a sideline, in the province of the farmer's wife, rather than part of the main business of the farm. While they were valued for their eggs and meat, their droppings spread as fertilizer and the feathers used in pillows, the farmer did not bother himself with poultry-keeping when he could get more for wheat, wool or meat.

Poultry farming began to burgeon in the latter half of the 19th century. New breeds were developed and poultry shows stimulated improvement in egg-laying and meat production. Some of these breeds have become almost extinct as modern breeds replaced them. There are three main groups of chicken breeds: layer, table and general-purpose. Another group is the fancy breeds which includes the bantams, the Yokohama with its enormous (6 metre (20-foot)) tail and other bizarrely feathered chickens. Bantams are very often no more than dwarf varieties of the standard breeds of domestic poultry.

Above; Helmeted guineafowl from Africa are rarely raised as farm animals. They are more likely to be kept for their ornamental appearance.

Left: A mixed flock of domestic geese includes white Emdens, and Chinese geese with the dark 'pigtail' down the back of the neck. Huge flocks of geese numbering many hundred are rarely seen nowadays as a way of farming them intensively has yet to be devised and goose meat is going out of favour.

To the chickens which had traditionally scratched around the farmyard, were added increasing numbers which were kept in a field set aside for the purpose. As the farmers came to rely more on artificial feeding, the chickens were given less ground in which to roam and eventually the battery farm was developed. Chickens now spend their lives indoors in a controlled environment which ensures the maximum production of eggs and meat.

Many wild birds lay a definite number of eggs. If a clutch is eaten by predators, the bird cannot lay again

that year. Other birds can replace lost eggs by laying extra. It seems that the bird recognizes that it has the right number of eggs in the nest through pressure on its breast and, if one is taken away, it lays another, until the clutch is complete. The duck family and the chicken family belong to the group which can replace lost eggs. The aim of chicken breeding has been to exaggerate this habit. The eggs are taken away as fast as they are laid so that the hen continues to lay. Once the clutch is complete a bird usually goes 'broody', as its instinct to incubate the eggs comes into action. Among layer breeds, the urge to go broody has almost disappeared. The hens merely continue laying. To renew the stock, eggs have to be hatched out in incubators.

The most famous layer is the Leghorn, a breed which comes from Italy. There are twelve varieties including the White Leghorn which is the world leader in egg production. The second most popular is the Minorca, another Mediterranean breed. However, the record for egg production is held by another breed, the Black Orpington. One laid 361 eggs in 364 days at an official test in New Zealand. The Leghorn holds the record for the weight of a single egg. An American hen laid a 453·6-gram (15·08-oz) egg with double yolk and double shell. Over the course of the 20th century there has been a continued rise in the

Above: Although it hardly appears beautiful, the Muscovy duck is another bird which is more often kept for ornament. Muscovies are descended from musk ducks native to South America.

Right: A duck keeps a watchful eye on her brood of fluffy ducklings. Plaintive quacks tell her if any are lost because she does not recognize them by sight. Her own quacks keep the ducklings near her until they are old enough to search for food on their own.

number of eggs laid by a single hen. In 1910 the average number of eggs laid in a year was 104; it is now 218. Moreover, the amount of food needed to produce these eggs has increased by only one half.

Specialized table breeds are few in number. They include the Dorking, La Bresse, Faverolle and Indian Game. They are large, heavy-bodied birds but they are, paradoxically, not very popular and most chickens appearing on the table come from the general-purpose breeds. These are the breeds which are household names. They include Rhode Island Red, Wyandotte, Plymouth Rock and Orpington. Most are American. The Rhode Island Red comes from a mixture of red jungle fowl, Shanghai, Leghorn, Cornish, Wyandotte and Brahma. In 1930, the New Hampshire was derived from the Rhode Island Red. The Wyandotte (pronounced Wine-dot) is also a mixture of breeds. These general-purpose chickens are good to keep in the farmyard because they lay nice brown eggs, continue production over the winter, and can be brought to the table. Commercial meat production comes from broiler houses where small chicks are reared intensively. One man can look after up to 50,000 chickens and, as they go to market when only three months old, he rears 200,000 a year. The growth of the chicks is quite incredible; they put on over 40 times their hatching weight in eight weeks, yet they eat much less than they did thirty years ago. This phenomenal productivity has been brought about by careful management, control of disease, improved

feeding and selected breeding. Broiler chickens are crossbreeds of several breeds and some of the pure breeds are becoming very rare.

Turkey farming has gone the same way as chicken farming with intensive rearing and considerable cross-breeding. The two species of wild turkey are natives of America. The ocellated turkey lives in Yucatan and Guatemala and the second, known simply as 'the turkey', was once found over much of the United States, Canada and Mexico, their numbers being now much reduced from hunting and destruction of their woodland home.

Turkeys were first domesticated by the Incas, long before the arrival of Europeans, and it was their only domestic animal apart from the dog. Some turkeys were brought back to Europe in 1523 or 1524. Forty years later flocks were being kept in several parts of Europe and they appeared on the English Christmas menu in 1585. Domestic turkeys were then taken back to America where they are now part of the traditional Thanksgiving dinner.

The origin of the name 'turkey' is something of a mystery. The Spaniards, who discovered the bird, called it the Indian fowl, as they thought that the land they were exploring was part of the Indies. The same misunderstanding of geography is repeated in the French *dindon*, coming from *d'Inde* – of India. The English name may be due to the first turkeys being imported by merchants from the Mediterranean and neighbouring coasts. These merchants were known as Turks and the bird would have been called a turkey fowl.

Until the end of World War II, turkey farming was a small scale enterprise as chicken farming had been. In a handbook of agriculture published in 1803, the author considers that turkeys are more profitable than any other bird for the amount of care they need. Small farms could keep small flocks of one cock and half a dozen hens. They breed extremely well and were fed cheaply on the surplus buttermilk or milk from dairy farming. In Ireland these fluids were mixed with a little oatmeal and shredded nettles to form a paste.

Nowadays turkeys are reared on large farms using crossbred strains which fatten rapidly. Modern breeds range from the Norfolk or Black, through bronze to white. White breeds are the most popular and there is a trend to produce smaller birds to fit into modern ovens.

Allowing for the greater amount of attention they required, geese used to be the most profitable of poultry. A single man might keep 1,000 adult geese and as each raises seven goslings, productivity was very good. The geese were pastured on grass or stubble fields and they were kept for more than their eggs and meat. Their fat – 'goose grease' – was used in ointments for skin troubles or as a protection against colds. The feathers were used to stuff pillows, for

feathering arrows and as quill pens. Quills from the right wing were more valuable because they angled over the writer's wrist. Presumably left-handed people were lucky because cheaper quills suited them! The main profit from geese lay in their feathers and the best price was obtained for feathers taken from live birds. Geese moult their feathers three times a year but, before they could be shed naturally, the farmer plucked them. If done at the right time, the feathers come away easily and do not hurt the bird. In the county of Lincolnshire, geese were plucked five times a year.

Domestic geese are descended from the greylag goose which breeds from Iceland across Europe and Asia. Domestication probably started in Stone Age times. Goslings tame very easily when taken from the wild, a practice which still takes place in places where greylags nest. Their natural gluttony makes them easy to fatten, and fat birds are unlikely to fly away. The Romans exploited this gluttony to stuff geese with a mixture of flour, milk and honey so that the liver became swollen. The result is *paté de foie gras*.

Above: Pigeons used to be important farm animals as young pigeons were an inexpensive source of fresh meat particularly in winter. Small pigeon cotes, inside which the pigeons nested, were built into the walls and roofs of barns or houses, and large ones were free-standing buildings.

Right: A Duck-winged Game cockerel watches attentively over his two hens. These chickens are lucky to be leading a free life where they can scratch for food on the road. Heavy motor traffic usually makes this a hazardous occupation and most farm chickens now spend their lives cooped up indoors in the interests of productivity and profit.

Right: Battery hens are condemned to a life of egg-laying without ever seeing a chick hatch. In return for regular square meals they are expected to lay about 200 eggs a year.

Far right: Another hen is living in more pleasant surroundings. In its nest of straw it is allowed to keep its eggs and incubate them. As the eggs are not removed it will stop laying and go broody.

The importance of geese in the economy of past centuries is shown by the Nottingham Goose Fair which was started in 1283. Huge flocks were reared in England, particularly in the eastern fenlands. Geese were even imported from Russia, Germany and Ireland for fattening. In Britain, goose farming is on the decline but it is still practised on a large scale in parts of continental Europe. The main breeds are the grey Toulouse and the white Emden or Embden. The second species to be domesticated is the Chinese goose which is similar to the greylag but the neck is longer and the male, or gander, has a knob at the base of the beak.

The farming of ducks is very similar to that of geese. It was largely a cottage industry but in some places duck rearing was practised on a large scale. Duck eggs were once more appreciated in Britain than they are today and the number of flocks has dwindled. A few ducks were often kept around the farm because they ate harmful grubs and did not require much attention. There were, however, two practices which

increased productivity. Egg laying was stimulated by letting the ducks indoors to keep warm by the kitchen fire or even under the bed. A large number of ducklings die of drowning if left with the duck, and they are also very vulnerable to crows and hawks on a pond, so the eggs were usually taken from the mother duck and brooded under a chicken in a coop.

Most domesticated ducks are descended from the wild mallard which ranges over Europe, parts of Asia and North America. The favourite British breed is the white feathered Aylesbury, which is traditionally reared around the town of that name. The chief American breed is the Pekin. These ducks are bred for their meat, whereas Khaki Campbells and Indian Runners are layers which average 300 eggs per year, which is more than the best chickens.

The muscovy duck has been domesticated on a small scale, although it is usually kept as an ornamental or fancy bird. It has no more connection with Russia, whose old name was Muscovy, than turkeys have with Turkey. The name comes from muskduck.

74

Muscovies are native to South America, where they had been domesticated long before the arrival of Europeans. The Spaniards brought some back to Europe and they are now kept for their meat. This is not so good as domestic mallard's but muscovies require a smaller area of water than do other ducks. The usual practice, however, is to cross muscovies with domestic mallards. The offspring are sterile but grow rapidly and are good to eat.

Chickens, turkeys, geese and ducks are reared in huge numbers the world over but there are some less common types of poultry. Pelicans were kept by the Ancient Egyptians as layers, and swans were farmed in mediaeval times. But the only two of any importance are guineafowl and pigeon.

Guineafowl come from Africa and were regarded as a luxury food by the Romans. After the fall of the Roman Empire they disappeared from Europe but they were rediscovered by Portuguese explorers on the west coast of Africa in the 16th century. This explains the English name because this part of Africa was known as Guinea. Guineafowl are still a luxury item for gourmets. They are reared in considerable numbers in Italy but they are no good for a mass market as they require too much food to be reared economically.

Pigeons, on the other hand, were once very important farm animals. They have been used in the past for carrying messages and, today, their homing instincts are exploited in racing. There are also many fancy breeds but pigeons were once a useful source of meat, particularly in regions where other poultry were not kept. Domestic pigeons are descended from the rock dove which nests on cliffs. Farmers and landowners built large dovecotes or pigeon towers whose inner walls were slotted with rows of small alcoves to attract the pigeons. Several hundred pairs of pigeons could be accommodated and the young pigeons, or squabs, were taken from the nest. As the pigeons nest all the year round the squabs provided welcome fresh meat in winter. The pigeons needed no feeding as they could forage for themselves in the fields.

Growing up on the Farm

One of the main aims of the farmer is to increase his stock. As many as possible of his animals must give birth or lay eggs and he must endeavour to ensure that as many of these offspring as possible should survive. Modern breeding programmes are striving to develop breeds which produce large litters or clutches. Sheep are bearing triplets or quadruplets rather than singletons or twins, and pigs produce huge litters. Unfortunately for some breeds, they have been selected for a particular shape or body and the actual birth is difficult. The farmer has to assist and, even with less awkward breeds, farmer or shepherd is in attendance to assist with difficulties. The ultimate in unnatural breeds is the Broad-breasted White Turkey whose body is so distorted as to make mating impossible. The breed is kept in existence through artificial insemination.

Another aim of modern breeding is to find good mothers. These will be females which produce plenty of milk for their offspring and also care for them. A bad mother may kill her litter either intentionally by attacking them or unintentionally by trampling or rolling on them. Because sows are careless mothers, pig pens are now constructed in such a way that the sow cannot crush her piglets; although Hampshire pigs make good mothers because they are not nervous, lie still while giving birth and are not likely to crush the piglets.

The offspring can also suffer through neglect. Inexperienced mothers, in particular, are likely to abandon their babies and the farmer has to take them in hand and rear them on the bottle. Hand rearing is necessary where a large litter becomes more than the mother can cope with.

The time immediately around the birth is most important for the later health and welfare of the young farm animal. As the time of birth approaches, the expectant mother's behaviour changes. A cow wanders away from the herd and grazes alone. Sows build nests out of straw or grass, having first scratched and rooted soil into a foundation. Sometimes the nest is so large, the sow disappears into it.

Immediately following the birth, the mother performs the vital task of learning her offspring's identity. This is very necessary in animals which live in herds as the family can be easily separated from each other among a mass of animals. The mother cow recognizes her calf by sight, smell and hearing. Cow and calf remain apart from the herd for several days and during this time they learn to recognize each other.

Far left: This calf is not growing up in natural surroundings. It is confined to an indoor pen and is being fed from a bucket. Note the long tongue which can clear stray drops of milk from the nostrils.

Left: Piglets of a Large White sow enjoy a feed in safety. The sow is kept in a pen which prevents her rolling and crushing the young. The piglets always feed from the same teat and, as the teats nearest the sow's head give the most milk, the piglets that feed from them grow fastest.

77

Above: One of these new-born lambs is still wet from birth and is being licked by its mother. This is when she learns its identity so that she can find it unerringly should they become separated. There is little chance of this happening at first because the lamb stays pressed to the ewe's flank.

Right: Twins are common in sheep. Like all baby mammals they are little more than bags of skin and bone when they are born. Their mother's milk soon fills them out, providing minerals and vitamins for growing bones and protein for developing muscles. It also supplies fat which gives energy and develops a fat layer to keep the baby animal warm.

Previous spread: Foals get to their feet and follow their mothers within an hour of birth. Shaky at first, they soon gain confidence in their movements and start to run around. At first they will not stray far from the security of the mare's side. Foals begin to nibble solid food when two weeks old but they are not weaned from the mother's milk until six to eight months.

The calf struggles to its feet very soon after birth and is walking in a few hours. It spends most of its time sleeping, while its mother grazes nearby. When the pair join the herd they tend to gather with other cows and calves. If they become separated for any reason the cow and calf low to each other until reunited. The bond between the two is slowly weakened until the calf drifts away to join a group of similarly-aged calves in a group that keeps together.

The early life of pigs is rather different. Apart from sharing its mother's attention with several brothers and sisters, the new-born piglet is more helpless than a calf. As the piglets are born, the sow assists them to her teats by pushing them with her snout and hoofs. For six to ten days, the piglets stay in the nest where they are kept warm by the sow, who will also sally forth in their defence if she senses danger. She calls to the piglets in warning and they either crouch motionless or run, scattering, to hide. Meanwhile the sow either attacks or tries to lead the intruder away.

If calves, lambs or piglets are separated from their mothers, both sides are distressed. They call and show every sign of being upset. A cow is upset for several days when she loses her calf, even if it is newborn, but newborn animals are much less worried by the separation. They have yet to form the vital bond and will happily transfer their affections to a foster parent. This can be another adult of their species, the farmer or one of his family or something quite inappropriate such as a cat or dog. A lamb used to being bottle-fed by the farmer's wife will happily stand by her apron hanging from the clothes line. For the lamb, the apron is identified with the person who provides the nourishing bottle of milk and becomes a symbol of security. If the lamb strays away and is suddenly frightened, it runs back to the protection of the apron.

A fixation on the mother or a mother-substitute is even more developed in poultry. Chicks and ducklings can run about and feed themselves very soon after hatching and must not get lost. As soon as they are able to run, they follow moving objects. At first they follow any moving object but after three days they follow only the mother bird. This fixation is called imprinting and, in nature, chicks and ducklings will imprint on their mother, but during the first three days of life they will imprint on any large, moving object as a substitute. A moving box, a dog or a person will do and, once imprinting has taken place, the little birds look on the object as 'mother' until it is time for the family to break up.

Life for a young animal is carefree. Mother supplies food and protection so there is plenty of time to play. Play is not confined to young animals, any more than it is to human children, but young animals are much more playful than adults. Sometimes they seem to play purely for fun. Nothing appears more pointless and full of careless enjoyment than the gambolling of a

Top: A Light Sussex hen calls her chicks to food. Different calls are used to lead them to roost or warn of danger.

Above: This gosling has happily accepted a bantam as its foster mother.

lamb or the bucking and prancing of a calf. Animals play most often when they should be full of fun and energy. They play more in fine weather than when it is cold and wet and when they are well fed. They also play when released from confinement.

It seems that animals play purely for the pleasure of the activity and not with any goal in view. On the other hand, the form that play takes looks very much like adult behaviour. Two calves may butt each other in mock-fights, and courtship behaviour is common. There is no doubt that this is not real fighting or courting because there is a lack of purposiveness and there is no decisive outcome – the players just drift away. It is often suggested that play is practice for adult life and even aimless activities like gambolling helps coordination of the limbs. If this is the case there is still no reason why there is not an element of enjoyment in their play. Human children do not play 'cops and robbers' as practice for adult life, hopefully, but for the enjoyment of exercise. If play is important, the lessons are probably more general. The animal is not learning specifically how to fight and court, it is learning generally about social relationships.

Farm Animals on Show

The aim of the farmer has always been to improve on nature; to produce animals which yield more meat, more milk or more eggs than wild animals. He selected, perhaps unconsciously at first, those animals which thrived best in the local conditions of climate and food supply.

Over the course of time there was a continual mixing and separation of farm animal stocks. Migration of tribes and military forays brought new blood swirling into areas where a period of peace and quiet had allowed well-defined breeds to form. So breeds formed and disappeared as new conditions rendered them unsuitable or interbreeding changed their character. Initially, each breed was very local in its distribution but improved transport has speeded the movements of both ideas and the products of those ideas.

In the 19th century, farmers interested in improving their stock banded together to form Agricultural Societies. The first in Britain was the 'Society of Improvers' in Scotland. The societies would meet for the members to view each others' animals, discuss their problems and successes, and some animals might change hands. The farmers began to list the qualities that they wanted in the animals and worked to produce them in their own stock. One of the pioneers of the Agricultural Revolution was Thomas Bakewell who painstakingly bred the British Longhorn as a beef animal.

Until Bakewell's time farmers had sold their fattest calves for veal and kept back the thinnest for breeding. They also kept smaller animals because they required less food in winter. Bakewell realized the now obvious fact that the way to improve the stock was to breed the best animals, weeding out inferior specimens. Another new idea was to breed closely-related animals. It is usually held that inbreeding is a bad thing – and human beings may not marry close relatives – but mating related animals which have desirable characteristics increases the chances of the offspring showing these common characteristics.

Novel ideas, such as Bakewell's theories of breed-

Far left: Winning prizes at an agricultural show is a good advertisement for a herd of farm animals. This Jersey bull, almost obscured by rosettes, will fetch a good price on the market and will be in demand for siring calves.

Left: British Saddleback pigs cleaned and combed for the show. Breeds are judged for specific characters. The closer that an animal conforms to the ideal shape and colouring laid down in the rules, the more likely it is to win a prize. Artificial specifications sometimes lead to a breed's value as a useful farm animal being reduced.

ing, are accepted by conservative farmers only if they can see the results literally in the flesh. Hence agricultural shows were founded as a forum for stockbreeders. The first show was held in 1797 and was organized by the 'Bath and West of England Society for the Encouragement of Agriculture, Manufactures and Commerce'. Since that year agricultural shows have been a very important part of the agricultural scene. The first shows were limited in their drawing capacity by problems of transport. Animals lost condition if they were driven far, and long distance movement was only possible if there was a convenient canal link. In 1801, a Hereford bull weighing 1,530 kilograms (30 cwts) arrived at Smithfield Market by water. Railways and, later, motor transport changed this and made agricultural shows national, and international, occasions.

It did not take long for agricultural shows to become competitive. Either the organizing society or a rich patron would put up prize money for the best animals in various classes or individual breeders would bet against each other. Each man would lay down a sum of money to back the conviction that his own animal would be judged the best. The prize animals, then as now, became valuable. The winning of a prize became a kind of guarantee of excellence which would attract farmers wishing to improve their herds. Unfortunately judges cannot be infallible and

Above: A ploughing match is always a popular event at a show.

Right: North American shows feature horse-drawing contests in which the teams draw metal sledges loaded with concrete. After each round, the load is increased, until only the winner is left.

there is the sad story of an Aberdeen Angus bull sold for a British record of £63,000 in 1963. Six months later it failed a fertility test.

Over the last two centuries breeds of farm animals have become standardized and Breed Societies define characters to which each breed should conform. The task of the show judges is then to decide which of the competitors comes nearest to perfection. The judges are accredited experts, often farmers or breeders who have a reputation for successful breeding themselves.

The visitor to a cattle show sees the parade of beautifully turned out animals, looking very different from the unkempt inhabitants of muddy pasture. The competitors, if they can be so called, are divided into classes. For instance, dairy cattle are classed as milking cows and dry cows and the former can be judged either on volume or on quality of their milk. Eventually the judges arrange the animals in order of merit and the winners are further beautified with decorations of rosettes and ribands.

What the ringside spectator does not see is the deeper investigation into the worth of the animals. A smartly turned-out animal which has all the correct

proportions of the breed is not necessarily valuable commercially and the judges have to enquire further into the nature of the competitors.

For animals which will end up on the table, it is often customary to judge their rate of growth because the farmer makes more profit if the time spent rearing the animal to a marketable weight is shortened. The growth rate is expressed as 'daily liveweight gain' which is estimated by subtracting the estimated birth weight from the current weight and dividing by the age in days. It is also necessary to know the quality of the meat. Our forefathers liked fatty meat and produced well padded animals. William Cobbett considered that a pig was not properly fat if it could walk 182 metres (200 yards) without stopping. The modern trend is for lean meat and a well rounded beast that looks so sleek in the show ring may fail to please when slaughtered. To satisfy this requirement, there are show classes in which the animals are judged first live then as dressed carcases.

Above: A line-up of Hereford steers at a show in Colorado are paraded for the judge's inspection. Note the neatly fluffed-out tail switches.

Left: Behind-the-scenes informality as a 9-year-old Percheron mare carries a child as old as herself. It takes as much behind-the-scenes organization and effort to mount an agricultural show as it does to mount a stage production.

A class that gives a good demonstration of an animal's breeding qualities is the 'family event' in which either father or mother are paraded with a selection of their offspring. If all are prizewinners, there can be no doubt that the pedigree is good.

For anyone who is not a farmer and has no interest in farming the parade of prize animals can be of little interest once their physical appearance has been admired, but there is more to a show than the exhibition of livestock. As well as the displays of aerobatics, military bands and other excitements which are put on to draw the crowds, there are the demonstrations and competitions of farming skills. There may be sheep-shearing, or ploughing or sheep-dog working.

Sheep-shearing contests are as old, if not older, than livestock shows. Shearing time on the farm has always been a time of festivity, as it was a natural high point in the farm year in the same way as the corn harvest. At the same period as the livestock shows were starting up, sheep-shearing contests were becoming something of a public exhibition. The fifth Duke of Bedford, who succeeded to the title in 1771, held sheep-shearing contests at Woburn which lasted for several days and attracted hundreds of spectators. In some ways these Shearing Shows were more like a modern agricultural show than the contemporary livestock shows. Apart from the actual contest there were exhibitions of animals and the latest farm equipment, and, as always, ample opportunity for discussions and arguments between farmers, breeders, dealers and butchers. In this way, new ideas and discoveries were transmitted around the farming world.

Sheep-shearing contests are nowadays only one of many events that take place in an agricultural show, except in Australia where contests take place on a large scale. Ploughing contests and sheepdog trials may take the form of independent occasions or they form part of a larger general show.

In ploughing matches, the contestants have to plough a set area of ground, the result being judged for neatness and regularity of the furrows. The soil has to be neatly turned over to make a firm bed to receive the seeds and the tops of neighbouring furrows have to be

level. It is also necessary to watch the 'ins and outs'. This is the way that the plough is put in and taken out at start and finish of the furrow. The well-organized matches today, which culminate in a world championship, held in Germany in 1978, started in simple challenges between rival ploughmen or as wagers between farmers as to who employed the best man.

In the sheep-dog trial, the shepherd has to move a small flock of sheep, usually four or five, around a course by remote control. In other words, he has to stand in one place and shout or whistle orders to his dog. Acting on these instructions, the dog guides the sheep through gaps in fences and finally into a small pen where they must be held secure. Sometimes a pair of dogs are employed and the flock has to be split in two. One dog holds half the sheep in a pen while the other takes the remainder around the course.

The ranch-type of farming in the United States and Australia has produced a different type of show – the rodeo. The name comes from the Spanish for 'round-up' and rodeo is the rowdy, action-packed, and dangerous equivalent of a sheep-shearing contest, ploughing match or sheepdog trial. It consists of competitions mainly based on the working skills of cowboy and stockman.

Rodeos started as informal competions when the cowboys had finished their cattle drives and they are now an important spectator sport with professional 'cowboys' working their way around an annual circuit of shows. Some of the events, such as steer wrestling and bull riding, are not really based on the cowboy's job. Steer wrestling involves riding alongside a galloping steer and leaping on it, grabbing its horns and throwing it off its feet. In bull riding, the cowboy has to stay on the back of a bucking bull. Neither activity is part of his normal work.

More realistic events are calf-roping and bronco-riding. Calf-roping involves catching and preparing a calf for branding. The calf is chased across the arena by the cowboy who lassos it, then throws himself from

his horse, flings the calf over and ties its legs together. Just before dismounting the cowboy fastens the lasso to the saddlehorn and his horse is trained to stop and keep the rope taut so that the calf's movements are restricted.

Bronco-riding is based on the old technique of training a horse, by riding it to exhaustion. The horse is placed in a restraining box, the cowboy mounts it and wraps a single rein around one hand and they are released into the ring. The horse has a special strap around its belly to encourage it to buck and the aim of the competition is to stay mounted for at least 10 seconds, without touching either the horse or rein with the free hand.

Australian rodeos have similar contests, together with their own 'camp-drafting'. This consists of cutting out a cow or steer from a group or 'camp' and guiding it through a course marked with stakes or oildrums. The animal is steered by nudging it with the horse's shoulder.

Above: A mixed bag of goats: Anglo-Nubian, British Toggenburg and British Saanen. They are competing for the prize awarded to the Best Kid.

Top. A top-class Saanen type milking goat displays her prizes. Points of good conformation include a long, level back, deep body and well-attached udder.

Above left: A judge examines a ram in a more informal line-up of animals. Tameness is clearly an asset appreciated by handlers and judges.

89

The Changing Scene

There has been a revolution in farming. All over the world people are leaving the country and flocking into the cities. One reason for this is that farming is becoming more mechanized. One man and a machine do the work previously done by a large force. Once, the whole community turned out to bring in the harvest. Reaping and threshing were performed by hand, with the assistance of horses or oxen to pull carts or trample on the threshing floor. Now the same two operations are carried out by a single man sitting atop a gigantic machine, the combine harvester. Stock farming is also more mechanized and intensive with some animals spending their whole lives cramped inside sheds. Furthermore, as farming practices change and small farms amalgamate, fields increase in size and farm buildings stand empty, slowly sliding into ruin.

Intensive farming is necessary to feed an increasing human population but it has led to an increasing nostalgia for what are thought to be the good old days of manual labour and low producivity. A return to the past is even becoming more practical as the rising price of oil, which is used in the manufacture of fertilizer and animal feed as well as a fuel, counteracts savings made by pruning the labour force. For one reason or another there are pockets among the intensively cultivated countryside where the old methods linger.

One farming practice that has gone from the country scene is the driving of flocks and herds on foot or hoof from farm to market. The countryside used to be criss-crossed by drove roads, some of great antiquity. The prehistoric roads of Britain were highways for the traffic of animals. Some, like the Berkshire Ridgeway, are now grassy tracks used only by ramblers or are 'green lanes' winding apparently nowhere through the fields. Others are now main trunk roads.

Left: The record for hand-shearing is 350 in one day but it will take this shepherd a long time to deal with his flock.

Right: Where fencing or walls are not good enough to restrain the most persistent escaper, a triangle of rods is often fixed round its neck to prevent it squeezing through gaps.

Although the history of drovers stretches back into antiquity, their heyday was in the 18th and early 19th centuries, during the Agricultural and Industrial Revolutions. Towns were becoming too large to feed themselves on local produce. Large quantities of animals had to be brought in from distant countryside and the only transport was by foot. In Britain, the general pattern was for cattle and sheep to be reared in the hills of Wales and Scotland and driven down to the lusher land of England for final fattening.

Droving was a large industry and the procession of herds and flocks was supplied by wayside inns and traditional grazing areas. There was even a need for blacksmiths because cattle were shod for the long journey. The life-style of the cattle drovers has been immortalized by Sir Walter Scott in his story *The Two Drovers*. They went into decline and as railways improved and offered a cheaper form of transport, the drove roads became constrained by enclosures of the countryside and tollgates.

Cattle and sheep were not the only animals to be driven long distances. Pigs, turkeys and geese were also transported down the drove roads. To protect their soft, webbed feet, geese were walked through a mixture of tar, sawdust and sand to form a tough but flexible sole. In Roman times flocks of geese were driven across the Alps into Italy, which puts

Hannibal's feat with his elephants into a different perspective!

The practice of droving lingered into the 20th century, when the widespread motor vehicles finally killed it off. Livestock are now carried by motor transport, packed together so that they do not injure themselves when the vehicle corners. Animals have,

Below: A rare scene in these days of factory farming. Farms are becoming too specialized to have room for families of chickens to scratch around for food in the farmyard. The trend is to farm larger numbers of animals on an intensive basis. This means that their activities are closely regulated and chickens are lucky to see the light of day.

therefore, been effectively removed from the roadside except in odd places where a goat or pony is staked out to graze, and in remote regions where poultry can still safely scratch by the roadside.

The disappearance of animals from the road has been matched by their retreat from the fields. Meat and dairy animals and poultry are brought indoors and their food cropped in the fields and brought to them. Finnish Landrace sheep have to remain indoors in winter because their wool is not waterproof but they produce twice as many lambs as their hardy ancestor the Soay sheep. But the major change to overtake farming is mechanization. Heavy horses have almost disappeared. They once did much more than draw ploughs and pull carts. At the turn of the century horses worked a wide variety of farm implements and machines which are now powered by internal combustion or electric motors. They pulled seed drills, harrows and rakes and worked stationary machines such as threshers and elevators by walking around a drive shaft in endless circles.

Below: Milking a cow by hand is learned with practice. It is a slow job and is only worthwhile if a few cows are kept. A large herd makes the investment in machine milking apparatus a practical necessity. It is faster and more hygienic.

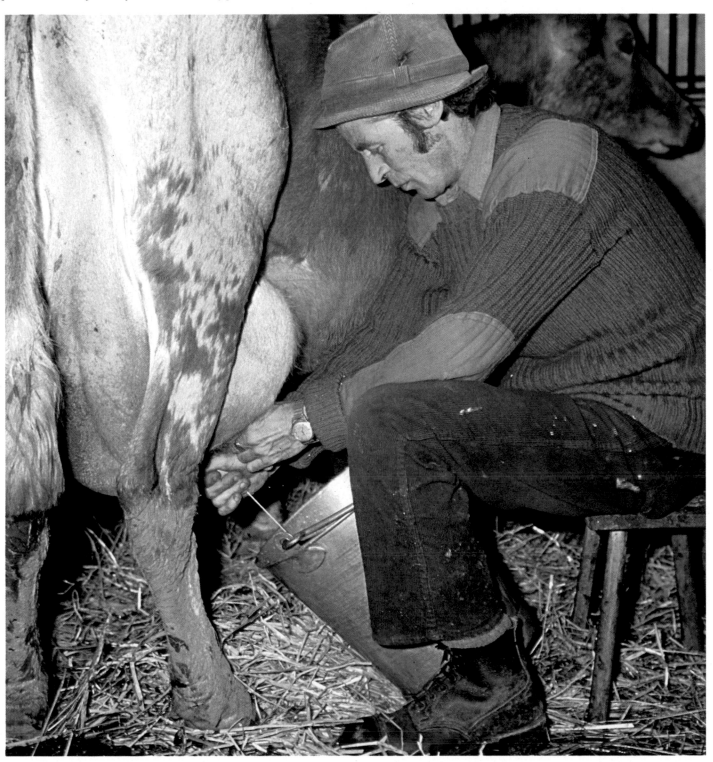

Above: Old farming methods linger in out-of-the-way places where farms are smaller and there is not sufficient money for modernization. Intensive farming would not allow this cow to wander by the roadside and the day's milk production would require more than half a dozen churns waiting to be collected.

Right: This exhibit at an agricultural show demonstrates the extent of the horse's role on farms before the invention of internal combustion engines. Horses were used to drive stationary machinery, such as this elevator, by walking in endless circles at the end of a crank. The crank's movement is transmitted to the machinery through a system of gears and rotating shafts or belts.

It may be a matter of regret that the days of the heavy horse are over but there is no doubt that mechanization is more efficient in nearly every way. A team of horses pulling a plough is a more magnificent sight than a tractor performing the same job at high speed and the oldtime ploughmen no doubt made a more professional job. Yet who nowadays would willingly get up at 4.00 in the morning and work through to the evening for a pittance?

The rising cost of labour and a desire for better working conditions has made mechanization essential. There is also the need for greater productivity to feed an increasing population which demands better food. The milkmaid squatting on her stool and the farmer's wife scattering grain for a bevy of chickens and ducks may fit the romantic rural image but milk and eggs would be extravagantly expensive if it were not for milking machines and automatic feeders. Cattle look better in the setting of a meadow studded with buttercups, but buttercups are mildly poisonous and specially sown leys grazed in strips are more efficient.

And chicken would be a luxury if it were not for broiler houses.

Yet the old ways are not completely dead. Even in regions where farming is run on factory lines, there are corners where cattle graze on old pastures. Even in the more industrialized countries horses can be seen drawing ploughs in earnest and not just at shows. Even in the United States horses are still at work. The Amish people of Pennsylvania use no machinery and, in Vermont, maple sap is carried on horse-drawn sledges. The horses know the route through the maple trees and learn when to start and stop without orders.

Preserving for Posterity

A few years ago the scientists at a poultry research unit in Scotland were investigating a serious problem among battery hens. They lay their eggs so easily that they do not bother to squat. The result was that the egg dropped from a height, the shell cracked and the industry lost hundreds of thousands of pounds each year. The solution hit upon by the scientists was to reduce the height of the drop by crossing the battery chickens with the short-legged Dumpy breed. Unfortunately this bright idea did not succeed for the simple reason that the Dumpy had disappeared. Nobody had been interested in the breed and it had become extinct.

The demise of the Dumpy is not unique. Many breeds of farm animals have lost favour and disappeared. The Cumberland pig was very common in the 1930's and it gave rise to such products as Cumberland ham and Cumberland sausages. But in 1960, the population was down to a single sow. The Lincolnshire Curly Coat pig was declared extinct in

Opposite: Longhorn cattle have had a long history. Descended from the extinct wild aurochs, they appear in Stone Age cave paintings and were transported across the Atlantic, where they became Texas Longhorns.

Below: The Soay sheep has been rescued from obscurity as it produces lean meat very efficiently and is resistant to diseases.

1971 but the announcement was premature. Two years later the last were slaughtered in a laboratory test.

The loss of these breeds may seem unimportant. There are hundreds of breeds of farm animals and it would appear reasonable to concentrate on those which are the most profitable in terms of easy rearing and quality of product. The Cumberland pig went out of favour because the bacon curers wanted a lean, long-bodied animal, like the Large White. The Cumberland was also a good 'farm pig', at home in a sty and unsuited to a modern farm-factory. In which case, its extinction does not appear to be any loss, but the story of the Dumpy chicken shows that judgement should not be too hasty.

There is a trend to concentrate on farming a few breeds of animal and in modern intensive farming crossbreds are increasingly reared. These are animals of mixed parentage rather than pure breeds. As a consequence many of the older breeds become rare and the chance of losing them is increased because of changing fashions. This is illustrated by the fortunes of British sheep. The hill breeds are not farmed intensively; they are allowed to roam almost wild. Most hill sheep are of the four main breeds: Cheviot, Scottish Blackface, Swaledale and Welsh Mountain but the remaining ten breeds are quite common except one, the rare Whitefaced Woodland. That so many breeds are still in use is due to the adaptation of each one to the environment of a particular region.

Top: The rare Portland sheep, now actively preserved, is an ancient breed once renowned for the delicate flavour of its meat.

Above: Jacob sheep are one of several breeds which grow more than one pair of horns.

Left: White cattle have been isolated in Chillingham Park in Northumberland since 1270. As they have escaped 700 years of cattle breeding, they represent a 'bank' of unique characteristics.

For lowland sheep, the situation is different. They are reared in small flocks under intensive conditions and it is quite easy for a farmer to get rid of one stock and set up with a new breed. The result is changing fashions in breeds. At one time the Wensleydale was popular. It was followed by Teeswater and then by the Blue-faced Leicester. As each breed went out of fashion it became rare.

The increasing number of farm breeds becoming rare or disappearing altogether has led to an organized movement for their protection. Sentiment is partly the reason. It is always sad to see something disappear, particular if it is a link with the past and there is the knowledge that it can never be brought back. These breeds can be thought of as part of our cultural heritage. They are as much a part of the nation's history as a period house or an antique table. They are the result of skilled work by many livestock breeders. Their original usefulness is past but they are preserved for enjoyment.

Interest in a bygone way of life is a popular pastime these days but the preservation of old breeds of farm animals has a more practical value. This is why the story of the Dumpy chickens is important. Livestock breeding seeks to increase production and to produce an animal which conforms to the current market preferences. This leads to uniformity and, if this goes too far, there will be no capacity for change or variety. We have seen on earlier pages how new breeds of cattle, sheep, pigs and poultry have been created by crossbreeding. This has been particularly important where European animals have been transported to the very different conditions of climate and vegetation in other parts of the world. The new breeds of Santa Gertrudis cattle, Poland China pigs and Corriedale sheep are examples of new breeds formed by cross-breeding existing types. There has, therefore, to be a 'genetic bank' of farm animals which might be useful some time in the future.

The importance of genetic banks is such that the Food and Agriculture Organization (FAO) of the United Nations runs a conservation of animal genetic resources project. Part of its work involves listing the world's breeds of farm animals. The Organization can then advise how an existing breed can be improved by crossing with a breed exhibiting a certain valuable trait. For instance the Devon Longwool sheep does not produce many lambs, so breeders brought in rams of the East Friesland, a breed which is very prolific, to mate with Devon Longwool ewes. The improved breed has almost doubled its birthrate. Similarly, the main Dutch breed, the Texel sheep, is being crossed with the rare Friesland Milk sheep to increase its lamb production. A hypothetical example is provided by the Soay sheep which sheds its wool naturally. If artificial fibres completely replaced wool it would be useful to develop breeds which did not need shearing and Soay blood would provide the starting point.

Another reason for maintaining old breeds is that much of recent breeding has aimed at high productivity types which flourish under intensive care. With feed and other costs soaring, there has been some return to animals which thrive in poor, marginal conditions. Such animals do not require expensive housing; they do not require top-grade pasturage or additional foods and the vet's bills are small. For instance, the Tamworth pig can be let loose in scrub or waste land to fend for itself and so be more economical

than the pampered Landrace. The Tamworth has the additional advantage that its rooting in the soil helps to clear scrubland so that it can be brought into cultivation. The Texas Longhorn is another breed which has returned to popularity because it is hardy enough to thrive in poor conditions.

The preservation of rare breeds is being undertaken at national as well as international level, and private farms and estates have done much to preserve some breeds. In North America, there is the American Minor Breeds Conservancy and the Association of Living Historical Farms and Agricultural Museums. Texas Longhorns, Durham cattle and Vermont Merino sheep are among those which are being bred on special farms. The Vermont Merino has wrinkled skin and it was thought that a greater area of skin would increase the wool yield.

In Britain, where there are a large number of rare breeds, preservation is organized by the Rare Breeds Survival Trust. This organization has been very successful in saving breeds and bringing them back onto farms. The complete restoration of a breed requires three steps.

First, the breed must be stopped from sliding into oblivion. Once it has gone, it can never be brought back. Some breeds have been caught only in the nick of time because their numbers have fallen to such a low ebb. There may be only a single small herd in existence. This is a very dangerous situation for two reasons. If there are only a score or so animals, they are in danger of becoming seriously inbred. The breed will degenerate through the appearance of genetic abnormalities. This is a difficult problem to overcome

unless a worldwide search reveals another group of animals.

The second danger is that disease or some other disaster could wipe out the herd. There were fears for the Chillingham Park cattle when the country suffered from an epidemic of foot-and-mouth disease. If the contagion had reached the park all the cattle would have had to be slaughtered. In the last war some White Park cattle were shipped to Canada for safety and, as they were easily visible from the air, others were painted blue and green for camouflage – an amazing sight from the ground!

The possibility of being wiped out by some disaster faced the North Ronaldsay sheep. These sheep live on the island of North Ronaldsay, in the Orkney group to the north of the Scottish mainland. The sheep of the Scottish islands regularly wander onto the shore to eat seaweed but the North Ronaldsay sheep are unique in that a stone wall running round the island confines them to the shore all the time. There is a little rough pasture above the shore but the bulk of the sheep's diet is tough brown seaweeds. North Ronaldsay sheep are a primitive breed, a relic dating back to Viking times and earlier. It is easy to see that a severe storm or perhaps a catastrophic oilspill could destroy these sheep, so the Rare Breeds Survival Trust has set up a second flock on another island, Linga Holm. There they found that this breed has a trait which might prove useful if bred into other sheep. The ewes are very aggressive towards predators and the lambs are very fleet-footed, so their survival rate is high.

Once the breed's survival has been safeguarded, the conservationists have time to make a thorough study of its characteristics. It is necessary to find out the specific qualities of the breed which make it worth saving. In the case of Shetland cattle, Tamworth pigs and Soay sheep, trials show that they produce a good yield on poor food. The Soay sheep is even more primitive than the North Ronaldsay, and probably the most primitive of all sheep. It comes from the islands of Soay and Hirta, of the St. Kilda group of seabound islands which lie west of the Hebrides. Sheep have lived on these islands since earliest times and they have retained the purity of the original British stock while mainland sheep were being developed into modern types. Until the human population was evacuated from St. Kilda in 1930, the sheep were confined to Soay, which means 'sheep island'. Then some were transferred to the main island of Hirta, where they still run wild. The Soay breed is very valuable, not only because it is a link between wild sheep and modern domestic sheep but because it has the qualities of hardiness which it may be useful to impart to other breeds. Also, the meat of the Soay is being evaluated to find whether it is worth developing the breed commercially.

Re-establishing a rare breed as a commercially useful farm animal is the third phase of its rehabilitation. The breed has to be promoted among farmers, with its advantages being shown off, and its breeding has to become a viable proposition. As we have already found, this has happened with some of the breeds which thrive in poor conditions, such as Longhorn cattle and Tamworth pigs.

When a breed has become extinct, its blood line may survive in a dilute form in crossbreeds. This has

Far left: The Gloucester Old Spot is an old breed which was rarely seen outside the Vale of Berkeley in the west of England. It was known as the Orchard Pig because it was fed on windfall apples and so converted waste from one crop into a valuable product. The breed went into decline until its good characters were recognized. Gloucester Old Spots are hardy, outdoor animals and are good mothers.

Left: The attractive golden-red Tamworth pig has always been a popular breed. Apart from its lean proportions, its dark pigmentation allowed it to thrive in tropical countries as it does not sunburn like white breeds. Because it is hardy it has recently become more popular in Europe as rising costs act against the intensive farming of the modern very productive but very delicate breeds.

Above: The Tamworth pig has an ancestry that goes back to the European wild boar. This is seen in the length of the snout. As part of an archaeological experiment, 'Iron Age' pigs were reconstructed by crossing a Tamworth with a wild boar.

Right: Bantams are miniature chickens, kept more for ornament than for eggs or meat. This brightly coloured cock belongs to the Old English Game breed. It is one of the most popular bantams and so preserves the characters of the birds once used in the sport of cock-fighting.

prompted breeders to try to reconstruct lost breeds, or even species. The two most famous 'reconstructions' are of the extinct ancestors of domestic cattle and horses.

The progenitor of cattle was the wild aurochs and the reconstruction of aurochs from domestic cattle by the Heck brothers has been described in Chapter 4. Lutz Heck also carried out breeding experiments with horses to reconstruct the tarpan.

The steppe tarpan was one of three subspecies of wild horse living in Europe and Asia. The forest tarpan and the steppe tarpan survived to the 19th century in eastern Europe, while Przwalski's horse still survives in small numbers in Mongolia and in larger herds in captivity. Before it died out, the forest tarpan had frequently been captured by Polish peasants who bred them into their Konik horses. When the wild tarpans died out, the domestic horses most resembling wild horses were gathered into two reserves, where they still survive. Lutz Heck has now crossed these Konik horses with Przwalski's horses to produce a horse which looks much like the original tarpan. Although there is tarpan blood in these horses, it should always be remembered that these cannot be considered as real tarpans.

The importance of realizing that these reconstructions are not the real thing holds with the so-called Iron Age pigs. In 1973 some pigs were specially bred for an experimental farm which would be used to investigate how Iron Age people lived and worked. All modern pigs have blood from Chinese pigs but something resembling the Iron Age pig was produced by crossing a Tamworth sow, a member of an old breed, with a wild boar, the progenitor of all European breeds.

Index

ACKNOWLEDGEMENTS
The publishers would like to thank the following
individuals and organizations for their kind permission
to reproduce the photographs in this book:—
G. V. Adkin 26, 98–99; Animal Photography Ltd.
(Sally Anne Thompson) 12–13, 20, 50; Ardea, London
7, (J. Bottomley and S. Bottomley) 96, (M. D.
England) 37, (Kenneth W. Fink) 9, (J. L. Mason)
68–69, (P. Morris) 16; Bio-Arts 31 below, 39, 56, 57
above, 57 below, 59, 70, 82, 84, 86–87, 89 above, 89
centre, 94–95, 101; J. Allan Cash Ltd. 8, 76; Bruce
Coleman Ltd. (Jane Burton) 21, 81 above, 97, 99
above, 99 centre, 102 centre, (Eric Crichton) 80 above,
(Leonard Lee Rue III) 34–35, (John Markham) 40,
(Fritz Prenzel 46–47, (Hans Rienhard) 19 above, 22,
29, 55, 65, 74, 90; Countrywide Livestock Ltd. 102
above; Robert Estall Photographs 23, 25, 32, 85; Susan
Griggs Agency Ltd. (Victor Engelbert) 4–5, (Adam
Woolfitt) Title page; Grant Heilman 17, (John Colwell)
33, 41 below, 47 above, 58, 63, 87 above; Eric Hosking
10; Jacana Agence de Presse (J. L. S. Dubois) 53,
(Brian Hawkes) 94 above, (J. M. Labat) 38, 44, 77,
78–79, (D. Lecourt) 36, (P. Lorne) 91, (Ray Tercafs)
66 above, (Jean-Paul Thomas) 66–67, (G. Trouillet)
48, 49; Frank W. Lane 11 below. (Arthur Christiansen)
15, (H. Schrempp) 92; Meat and Livestock
Commission 51 above; Jane Miller 71; The Natural
History Photographic Agency (Joe B. Blossom) 64,
72–73, (Douglas Dickens) 6, (L. Hugh Newman) 62,
(M. Savonius) 69 above, 72, (Philip Wayre) 11 above;
Oxford Scientific Films Ltd. Endpapers, 14, 27, 41
above, 75, 80 below; Photo Library International,
Leeds 24, 52; Spectrum Colour Library 28, 60–61,
88–89, 93; Tom Stack and Associates (D. Dickinson)
30, 42–43; John Topham Picture Library 45; The
Wildfowl Trust (Joe B. Blossom) Front and back
jacket, 51 below, 81 centre, 83, 100; The Thomas A.
Wilkie Company Ltd, 18–19, 54.
Picture Research:— Diana Korchien

PDO 79-142